McDougal Littell

MATH

Course 3

Larson   Boswell   Kanold   Stiff

CHAPTER 2

Resource Book

The Resource Book contains a wide variety of blackline masters available for Chapter 2. The blacklines are organized by lesson. Included are support materials for the teacher as well as practice, activities, applications, and project resources.

McDougal Littell

A DIVISION OF HOUGHTON MIFFLIN COMPANY

Evanston, Illinois • Boston • Dallas

Contributing Authors

The authors wish to thank the following individuals for their contributions to the Chapter 2 Resource Book.

Christine Cox

Donna Foley

Rebecca Salmon Glus

Julie Groth

Mark Johnson

Michelle McCarney

Leslie Palmer

Jessica Pflueger

Donna Rose

Monica Single

ISBN 13: 978-0-618-74161-8
ISBN 10: 0-618-74161-5

3456789–VEI–10 09 08 07 06

Contents

CHAPTER 2 Integer Operations

Contents

Contents

Descriptions of Resources

This Chapter Resource Book is organized by lessons within the chapter in order to make your planning easier. The following materials are provided:

Parents as Partners This guide helps parents contribute to student success by providing an overview of the chapter along with questions and activities for parents and students to work on together.

Teaching Guide with Lesson Plan The Teaching Guide provides essential questions, lesson ideas, and classroom strategies to help teachers easily create an engaging class, lead meaningful class discussions and increase depth of student understanding. A comprehensive list of available resources is provided in the Lesson Plan section to make planning easier.

Activity Masters These blackline masters make it easier for students to record their work on selected activities in the Student Edition, or they provide alternative activities for selected lessons.

Technology Activities with Keystrokes Keystrokes for various models of calculators are provided for each Technology Activity in the Student Edition where appropriate, along with alternative Technology Activities for selected lessons.

Practice A, B, and C These exercises offer additional practice for the material in each lesson, including application problems. There are three levels of practice for each lesson: A (basic), B (average), and C (advanced).

Study Guide These pages provide additional instruction, worked-out examples, and practice exercises covering key concepts and vocabulary in each lesson.

Quick Catch-Up for Absent Students This handy form makes it easy for teachers to let students who have been absent know what to do for homework and which activities or examples were covered in class.

Problem Solving Workshops These blackline masters provide extra problem solving opportunities in addition to the workshops given in the textbook.

Challenge Practice These exercises offer challenging practice on the mathematics of each lesson for advanced students.

Chapter Review Games and Activities This worksheet offers fun practice at the end of the chapter and provides an alternative way to review the chapter content in preparation for the Chapter Test.

Projects with Rubric These projects allow students to delve more deeply into a problem that applies the mathematics of the chapter. Teacher's notes and a 4-point rubric are included. The projects include a real-life project, a cooperative project, and an independent extra credit project.

Cumulative Practice These practice pages help students maintain skills from the current chapter and preceding chapters.

Name _____ Date _____

Parents as Partners

For use with Chapter 2

Chapter Overview One way you can help your student succeed in Chapter 2 is by discussing the lesson goals in the chart below. When a lesson is completed, ask your student the following questions. "What were the goals of the lesson? What new words and formulas did you learn? How can you apply the ideas of the lesson to your life?"

Lesson Title	Lesson Goals	Key Applications
2.1: Integers and Absolute Value	Graph and order integers. Find absolute value. Find opposites.	• Global Positioning System • Eyeglasses • Lake Evaluations • Space Shuttle Launch
2.2: Adding Integers	Add integers.	• School Fair • Checking Account • Mexico • Chemistry
2.3: Subtracting Integers	Subtract integers. Evaluate variable expressions.	• SOFAR Channel • Game Shows • Dinosaur Periods
2.4: Multiplying Integers	Multiply integers. Evaluate expressions with integers.	• Scuba Diving • Video Games • Stock Market
2.5: Dividing Integers	Divide integers. Find a mean.	• Temperatures • Musical Instrument • Reindeer
2.6: Number Properties	Use properties to evaluate expressions.	• Tour Biking • Juice Box • Super Bowl • Paycheck
2.7: The Distributive Property	Use the distributive property. Find a combined area. Combine like terms.	• Architecture • Flip-Flops • Souvenirs • Mural
2.8: The Coordinate Plane	Identify and plot points in a coordinate plane. Find perimeter.	• City Block • Fruit • Phone Calls

Know How to Take Notes

Noting Vocabulary is the strategy featured in Chapter 2 (see page 52). Encourage your student to write down not only the new vocabulary words they encounter, but also examples to illustrate how they are used. This practice helps to take the vocabulary from an abstract definition to a practical level. Having vocabulary in an easy to find notebook format also helps your student save time when he or she needs to look up a word or study for tests and quizzes.

Name _____ Date _____

Parents as Partners

For use with Chapter 2

Key Ideas Your student can demonstrate understanding of key concepts by working through the following exercises with you.

Lesson	Exercise
2.1	Use a number line to order the integers and integer expressions from least to greatest. **a.** $0, -1, -(-1), \lvert-3\rvert, -2$ **b.** $4, \lvert3\rvert, -2, -5, -\lvert3\rvert, 2$
2.2	Your family is having a garage and bake sale. The amounts below include the costs and amounts earned. How much, if any, profit was there? Rent tables: $35; Stickers for pricing: $6; Cookies sold: $18; Advertisement: $15; Clothing sold $53; Toys sold: $42.
2.3	A local trucking company has to move 25,000 pounds of salt to prepare for the upcoming winter. They have already moved 13,290 pounds. How much more do they have to move?
2.4	Find the product. **a.** $-169(8)$ **b.** $17(9)$
2.5	Find the quotient. **a.** $\dfrac{-414}{-18}$ **b.** $\dfrac{78}{-6}$
2.6	Evaluate the expression using mental math. Name the properties you used. **a.** $8 \cdot (3 \cdot 5)$ **b.** $17 - 19 + 33$
2.7	Find the area of each rectangle. Then find the total area of the 2 rectangles. **a.** 7 cm; 4 cm, 12 cm **b.** 4 ft, 5 ft; 18 ft
2.8	Plot and connect the given points. Then identify the resulting figure and find its perimeter. **a.** $(1, 6)$ **b.** $(-7, 6)$ **c.** $(-7, -2)$ **d.** $(1, -2)$

Home Involvement Activity

Directions: Pick a point in your room to be the origin of a coordinate plane. From there, measure the dimensions of your room. On graph paper, plot the dimensions of your room using your coordinate plane measurements. Find the perimeter and area of your room.

Answers
2.1: a. $-2, -1, 0, 1, 3$ **b.** $-5, -3, -2, 2, 3, 4$ **2.2:** $57 **2.3:** 11,710 lb
2.4: a. -1352 **b.** 153 **2.5: a.** 23 **b.** -13 **2.6: a.** 120; Commutative Property
of Multiplication, Associative Property of Multiplication **b.** 31; Commutative Property
of Addition **2.7: a.** $28\ cm^2 + 84\ cm^2 = 112\ cm^2$ **b.** $90\ ft^2 + 72\ ft^2 = 162\ ft^2$
2.8: square; 32 units

Games Support Master

For use with pages 54–55

Four in a Row

Choose 16 of the 24 answers to fill in the squares below.

168	196	240	315	338	342
352	361	405	414	418	441
516	522	529	595	720	792
832	851	918	961	975	1020

Name _____ Date _____

Games Support Master

For use with pages 54–55

Expression Cards

12×14	19×22	23×18	18×29
21×15	30×34	37×23	43×12
26×13	35×17	32×26	31×31
32×11	40×18	19×19	24×33
21×21	14×14	23×23	39×25
16×15	18×19	15×27	27×34

LESSON 2.1 Teaching Guide

Key Concept

You can compare integers by graphing them on a number line. On a number line, the greater integer is located farther to the right. The distance between a number and zero on a number line is the absolute value of the number. Two numbers are opposite if they have the same absolute value and different signs.

Teaching the Lesson

Differentiating Instruction: See the Teacher's Edition side column notes on pages 59 and 60 and the notes on differentiating instruction in the *Course 3 Best Practices Toolkit*.

Teaching Notes and Suggested Questions: See the Teacher's Edition side column on page 58.

Activity Generator: See the Activity Generator Support Manual.

Animated Math: You may want to include the animation on page 60 in your lesson.

Starting the Lesson

Connect to Real Life One way to introduce the concept of integers is to connect it to a situation that is familiar to students, such as temperatures.

Alternative Lesson Starter

You can also introduce the concept of integers by using time, such as using years B.C. and A.D. Students will realize that a year B.C. is represented by a negative integer and a year A.D. is represented by a positive integer.

Questions to Start the Lesson

1. Mark writes down the low temperatures (in degrees Fahrenheit) for 7 days in his town, as shown below. Order the integers from least to greatest.

   $4, -5, 0, 2, -7, -1, 6$

2. Mark accidentally wrote the opposites of the low temperatures. Write the opposites of the integers in Exercise 1 to find the actual low temperatures.

3. Order the actual low temperatures from Exercise 2 from least to greatest.

Common Student Errors

- Students may have difficulty understanding that when they see absolute value symbols in an expression that does not mean the result is always positive. For example, $-|7|$ is -7 because you take the opposite of the absolute value.

  Tip You may want to break this down as an order of operations type problem. First, evaluate $|7|$, and then take the opposite.

Example: Simplify $-|-24|$.

Student answer: 24

First, evaluate $|-24|$, which is 24, and then take the opposite of 24.

The correct answer is -24.

Teaching Strategy of the Day

Asking Questions Avoid labeling questions as "easy" or "hard." Students that cannot answer an "easy" question will believe the math is too difficult for them.

Teacher's Name _____ Class _____ Room _____ Date_____

Lesson Plan
Standard Schedule: 1 day lesson   Block Schedule: 0.5 day lesson with 2.2

GOAL   **Study integers.**

State Standards _____

Focus and Motivate	**Starting Options**
	____ Homework Check (1.7): TE p. 40; Answer Transparencies
	____ Daily Homework Quiz (1.7): TE p. 43
	____ Warm-Up: Transparencies
	____ Starting the Lesson Questions: Teaching Guide
	____ Motivating the Lesson: TE p. 57

Teach   **Teaching Options**

____ Alternative Lesson Openers: Electronic Classroom
____ Classroom Activity: Activity Generator
____ Examples 1–3: PE pp. 57–58
____ Extra Examples 1–3: TE p. 58
____ Real World Problem Solving: Chapter Resource Book p. 13
____ Notetaking Guide pp. 23–24

Checking for Understanding

____ Closing the Lesson: TE p. 58
____ Guided Practice Exercises: PE pp. 57–58

Practice and Apply   **Assigning Homework**

____ Basic: Day 1: pp. 59–61 Exs. 1–20, 22–32 even, 44–51, 55–59
____ Average: Day 1: pp. 59–61 Exs. 1, 2–14 even, 15–41*, 44–52, 55–59
____ Advanced: Day 1: pp. 59–61 Exs. 1, 2, 15, 16, 21–43*, 47, 49–54*, 58, 59
____ Block: pp. 59–61 Exs. 1, 2–14 even, 15–41, 44–52, 55–59 (with 2.2)
____ Practice Masters: Chapter Resource Book pp. 7–9 (Levels A, B, or C)

Assess and Reteach   **Differentiating Instruction**

____ Study Guide: Chapter Resource Book pp. 10–11
____ Tutorial Software
____ Challenge: Chapter Resource Book p. 14
____ Remediation and Intervention Package: _____
____ English Language Learners Package: _____

Preparing for Standardized Tests

____ Standardized Test Practice: PE pp. 59–61 Exs. 15, 46, 47, 49, 59

Assessing the Lesson

____ Daily Homework Quiz (2.1): TE p. 61 or Transparencies

Name _____ Date _____

Practice A

For use with pages 57–61

Complete the statement.

1. Whole numbers and their corresponding negative numbers are _____.

2. Negative integers are _____ than zero.

3. Positive integers are _____ than zero.

4. The absolute value of a number is the distance between _____ and _____ on a number line.

5. Two numbers are _____ if they have the same absolute value but different signs.

Use a number line to order the integers from least to greatest.

6. $6, 4, -3, -5, -9, -10, 7, 1$

7. $7, -4, 3, 0, -21, -36, 14$

8. $38, -38, -34, -42, 10, -18$

9. $0, -1, -4, -15, -24, 17, 5, 24$

Write the opposite and the absolute value of the integer.

10. 12 **11.** -4 **12.** 3 **13.** -15

Complete the statement with $<$ or $>$.

14. -7 ____ 3 **15.** 6 ____ 1 **16.** -5 ____ -2

17. 0 ____ 12 **18.** -9 ____ -10 **19.** 3 ____ -3

Match the integer expression with the verbal expression.

20. $-|5|$ **A.** the opposite of negative five

21. $|-5|$ **B.** the absolute value of five

22. $-|-5|$ **C.** the opposite of the absolute value of negative five

23. $-(-5)$ **D.** the absolute value of negative five

24. $|5|$ **E.** the opposite of the absolute value of five

Simplify the expression.

25. $|-8|$ **26.** $-(-4)$ **27.** $-|-14|$

28. $-|-9|$ **29.** $-[-(-3)]$ **30.** $-|-10|$

31. A part of Death Valley, near Badwater, lies 282 ft below sea level. Write an expression that represents the distance in feet of this elevation from sea level.

LESSON 2.1 Practice B

For use with pages 57–61

Does the given arrow show the location of the *positive* integers or the *negative* integers?

1. A

2. B

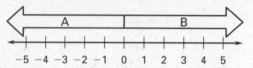

Order the integers from least to greatest.

3. 17, −24, −16, −8, 7, 2, 23

4. −16, −24, −38, 25, 11, −56, 102, −136

5. −7, −5, 2, −1, 4, 6, −10, 0

6. 8, −15, 17, −39, −51, 73, −84

Write the opposite and the absolute value of the integer.

7. 7

8. −25

9. 106

10. −241

Complete the statement with < or >.

11. −6 ____ 4

12. −2 ____ −4

13. 0 ____ 8

14. −11 ____ −3

15. 31 ____ −16

16. −24 ____ −28

Match the integer expression with the verbal expression.

17. $-|12|$

A. the opposite of negative twelve

18. $|-12|$

B. the absolute value of twelve

19. $-|-12|$

C. the opposite of the absolute value of negative twelve

20. $-(-12)$

D. the absolute value of negative twelve

21. $|12|$

E. the opposite of the absolute value of twelve

Simplify the expression.

22. $|-15|$

23. $-(-9)$

24. $|-16|$

25. $-|-6|$

26. $-(-|49|)$

27. $-[-(-34)]$

In Exercises 28–30, use the table at the right. It shows the distances of the runners from the finish line when the winner won the race.

28. Who won the race?

29. Who finished farther back, Sarah or Tamika?

30. Arrange the girls' names in order from first-place to last-place finish.

Runner	Distance (ft)
Sarah	−16
Beth	−2
Juanita	0
Tamika	−9
Ingrid	−36

Name _____ Date _____

Practice C
For use with pages 57–61

Order the integers from least to greatest.

1. 4, −7, 3, −5, 0, −1, 1, 6

2. −17, 28, 34, −29, −31, −45, 67

3. −88, 53, 41, −27, −104, −91, −73, 59

4. 190, −214, −506, 246, 308, 459, −716, −463

Write the opposite and the absolute value of the integer.

5. −44   **6.** 85   **7.** −137   **8.** 2461

Complete the statement with < or >.

9. 8 ____ −7   **10.** −23 ____ −35   **11.** 103 ____ 301

12. −14 ____ 0   **13.** 16 ____ −18   **14.** −41 ____ −76

Write the integer expression that corresponds with the verbal expression.

15. the opposite of negative fourteen

16. the absolute value of fourteen

17. the opposite of the absolute value of negative fourteen

18. the absolute value of negative fourteen

19. the opposite of the absolute value of fourteen

Simplify the expression.

20. $|-13|$ **21.** $-(-21)$ **22.** $-|-(17)|$

23. $-|43|$ **24.** $-(-|58|)$ **25.** $-[-(-37)]$

Order the numbers from greatest to least.

26. $-34, |-16|, |24|, -(-106), -|-81|$ **27.** $|-15|, -85, -|72|, -(-31), -|26|$

28. $-43, |-31|, -|36|, -|39|, -(-34)$ **29.** $-(51), -(-55), 63, -[-(-73)], (-|-49|)$

In Exercises 30–32, use the table that shows the elevations of some places relative to sea level.

30. Which place has the lowest elevation?

31. Arrange the elevations in order from lowest to highest.

32. Which place has a lower elevation, Lake Assal or Bahia Blanca?

Place	Elevation
Mt. Everest	29,035 feet
Mt. Kilimanjaro	19,340 feet
Dead Sea shore	−1312 feet
Lake Assal	−512 feet
Bahia Blanca	−138 feet

Name _____ Date _____

2.1 Study Guide

For use with pages 57–61

GOAL Study integers.

VOCABULARY

Whole numbers and their corresponding negative numbers are **integers.**

Negative integers are less than zero. They lie to the left of 0 on a number line.

Positive integers are greater than zero. They lie to the right of 0 on a number line.

The **absolute value** of a number is the distance between the number and zero on a number line, written as $|n|$.

Two numbers are **opposites** if they have the same absolute value but different signs.

EXAMPLE 1 ## Graphing and Ordering Integers

Below are the freezing points of various substances. To find which substance has the lowest freezing point, graph each integer on a number line.

Substance	Freezing Temperature (°F)
Water	32
Antifreeze and water	−32
Sea water	28
Gasoline	−36

Solution

Order the numbers from least to greatest: −36, −32, 28, 32.

Answer: Gasoline has the lowest freezing point at −36°F.

Exercises for Example 1

Order the integers from least to greatest.

1. −8, 5, −2, 0, 6

2. −12, 15, 3, 9, −6

3. 4, −4, 0, 16, −7

4. −5, −7, −3, 2, −4

Name _____ Date _____

Study Guide
For use with pages 57–61

EXAMPLE 2 ## Finding Absolute Value

An eyeglass prescription is given as a positive or a negative number. A prescription of a farsighted person is positive. A prescription of a person who is nearsighted is negative. The greater the absolute value, the stronger the prescription. Which prescription is stronger, -2.75 or 0.25?

Solution

$|-2.75| = 2.75$ and $|0.25| = 0.25$

Answer: The prescription of -2.75 is stronger because $2.75 > 0.25$.

EXAMPLE 3 ## Finding Opposites

Write the opposite of the integer.

   a. -4 The opposite of -4 is 4.

   b. 10 The opposite of 10 is -10.

   c. $|-6|$ Because $|-6| = 6$, the opposite of $|-6|$ is -6.

Exercises for Examples 2 and 3

Write the opposite of the number.

  5. 7 **6.** -1 **7.** $\left|\dfrac{1}{2}\right|$

  8. $|-2|$ **9.** $|-62|$ **10.** $|26.5|$

Copy and complete the statement with $<$ or $>$.

  11. 7 _____ -5 **12.** -11 _____ -6

  13. -9 _____ 2 **14.** -12 _____ -11

  15. 2 _____ -3 **16.** 0 _____ -4

Name _____ Date _____

2.1 Quick Catch-Up for Absent Students

For use with pages 57-61

The items checked below were covered in class on (date missed) _____

Lesson 2.1: Integers and Absolute Value

____ **Goal:** Study integers. (pp. 57–58)

Material Covered:

____ Example 1: Graphing and Ordering Integers

____ Guided Practice for Example 1

____ Example 2: Finding Absolute Value

____ Reading

____ Example 3: Finding Opposites

____ Guided Practice for Examples 2 and 3

Vocabulary:

integers, p. 57   negative integers, p. 57

positive integers, p. 57   absolute value, p. 58

opposites, p. 58

____ Other (specify)

_____

Homework and Additional Learning Support

____ Textbook (specify) pp. 59–61

_____

____ *Study Guide* worksheet (specify exercises)

____ @*HomeTutor* for Lesson 2.1

Real-World Problem Solving

For use with pages 57–61

Meteorology

Meteorology is a science that deals with the atmosphere. One branch of meteorology studies weather and weather forecasting. Meteorologists use scientific methods to predict what the weather will be.

Use the following information in Exercises 1–4.

José is the son of a farmer. For as long as José can remember, the weather has been a favorite topic of conversation among his parents and other farmers. Farmers are dependent on the weather to grow their crops. They need enough rain for the crops to grow, but not so much rain that everything is ruined. José has decided to be a meteorologist when he grows up. To learn more about precipitation, José set up a project. He measured the height of a bucket, marking each inch with a black pen. He labeled the 5-inch mark with a "0," and then filled the bucket up with water to the "0" mark. José set the bucket outside to catch rain. José planned to measure the water level once each month from March until October. After recording each measurement, he would empty the bucket and refill it to the "0" mark. His measurement would include the accumulated effects of rain and evaporation. These are the measurements that José recorded:

Month	Water Level
March	+3 inches
April	+6 inches
May	+8 inches
June	−1 inch

Month	Water Level
July	−3 inches
August	−2 inches
September	+1 inch
October	+2 inches

1. In which month did the most water accumulate?

2. In which month did the greatest loss of water occur?

3. What is the difference of the accumulation level in May and the accumulation level in July?

4. Put the months in order, beginning with the month that had the greatest loss of water and ending with the month that had the greatest accumulation.

Name _____ Date _____

Challenge Practice

For use with pages 57–61

Tell whether the statement is *always*, *sometimes*, or *never* true. Give examples to justify your answer.

1. The opposite of an integer is negative.

2. The absolute value of an integer is greater than the integer.

3. The opposite of the absolute value of an integer, except for zero, is positive.

4. The opposite of an integer is different from the absolute value of the integer.

5. The opposite of the opposite of an integer is the same as the integer.

In Exercises 6–8, use the equation $|x + y| = -|x + y|$.

6. Name a pair of values for x and y that makes the statement false.

7. Name three different pairs of values for x and y that make the statement true.

8. Describe the relationship between the values of x and y that makes the statement true.

Teacher's Name _____ Class _____ Room _____ Date_____

Teaching Guide

Key Concept

You can use a number line to add integers. To add a positive integer, move to the right. To add a negative integer, move to the left. You can also add integers by using absolute values. If the two numbers have the same sign, you add the absolute values and use the common sign. If the two numbers have different signs, you subtract the lesser absolute value from the greater absolute value and use the sign of the number with the greater absolute value.

Teaching the Lesson

Differentiating Instruction: See the Teacher's Edition side column notes on pages 65 and 66 and the notes on differentiating instruction in the *Course 3 Best Practices Toolkit*.

Teaching Notes and Suggested Questions: See the Teacher's Edition side column on page 64.

Activity Generator: See the Activity Generator Support Manual.

Animated Math: You may want to include the animation on page 66 in your lesson.

Starting the Lesson

Connect to Prior Learning Be sure that students can recall the following ideas:

- integer (p. 57)
- absolute value (p. 58)
- sum (p. 764)

Alternative Lesson Starter

You can also introduce the concept of adding integers by using an allowance (positive integers) given weekly for a certain number of weeks along with spending using money from the allowance (negative integers).

Questions to Start the Lesson

1. Is 0 an integer?

2. What is absolute value? Can the absolute value of a number be negative?

3. Suppose $|a| > b$. Is it always true that a must be greater than b?

3. Find the sum: $-1.45 + 3.16$.

Common Student Errors

- Students may try to add integers without fully understanding how to use the rules for adding integers. Make sure that all students have a solid understanding of absolute value before teaching the rules for adding integers.

Tip Students may be confused by the parentheses in Example 3. Point out, in this case, that parentheses are used for ease in reading. The expression $-84 + 0 + (-124)$ is easier to read than $-84 + 0 + -124$. The parentheses do not affect the sum.

Teaching Strategy of the Day

Motivating Students Be consistent. Assign homework everyday.

Teacher's Name _____ Class _____ Room _____ Date _____

Lesson Plan

Standard Schedule: 1 day lesson   Block Schedule: 0.5 day lesson with 2.1

GOAL   Add integers.

State Standards _____

Focus and Motivate

Starting Options

____ Homework Check (2.1): TE p. 59; Answer Transparencies
____ Daily Homework Quiz (2.1): TE p. 61
____ Warm-Up: Transparencies
____ Starting the Lesson Questions: Teaching Guide
____ Motivating the Lesson: TE p. 63

Teach

Teaching Options

____ Alternative Lesson Openers: Electronic Classroom
____ Classroom Activity: Activity Generator
____ Examples 1–4: PE pp. 63–65
____ Extra Examples 1–4: TE p. 64–65
____ Notetaking Guide pp. 25–27

Checking for Understanding

____ Closing the Lesson: TE p. 65
____ Guided Practice Exercises: PE pp. 63–65

Practice and Apply

Assigning Homework

____ Basic: Day 1: pp. 65–67 Exs. 1–22, 24–34 even, 36–38, 48–54, 56, 59–65
____ Average: Day 1: pp. 65–67 Exs. 1, 10, 11, 12–22 even, 24–36, 48–56, 59–65
____ Advanced: Day 1: pp. 65–67 Exs. 1, 11, 24–47*, 53–58*, 65
____ Block: pp. 65–67 Exs. 1, 10, 11, 12–22 even, 24–36, 48–56, 59–65 (with 2.1)
____ Practice Masters: Chapter Resource Book pp. 17–19 (Levels A, B, or C)

Assess and Reteach

Differentiating Instruction

____ Study Guide: Chapter Resource Book pp. 20–21
____ Tutorial Software
____ Challenge: Chapter Resource Book p. 23
____ Remediation and Intervention Package: _____
____ English Language Learners Package: _____

Preparing for Standardized Tests

____ Standardized Test Practice: PE pp. 66–67 Exs. 11, 39, 56, 57, 59, 66

Assessing the Lesson

____ Daily Homework Quiz (2.2): TE p. 67 or Transparencies

Name _____ Date _____

Practice A

For use with pages 62–67

1. What addition problem does the number line show? What is the sum?

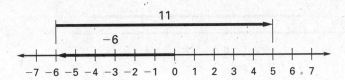

Use a number line to find the sum.

2. $-2 + 4$ **3.** $7 + (-8)$ **4.** $-6 + (-3)$

Complete the rule for adding integers without using a number line.

5. If the integers have the same sign, then add the _____ and use the common sign.

6. If the integers have different signs, then _____ the lesser absolute value from the greater absolute value. Use the _____ of the number with the greater absolute value.

In Exercises 7–15, find the sum.

7. $-23 + 31$ **8.** $-47 + 0$ **9.** $-38 + (-54)$

10. $-49 + (-121)$ **11.** $-15 + 15 + (-23)$ **12.** $-12 + 37 + (-54)$

13. $-83 + 41 + 63$ **14.** $-27 + 56 + (-85)$ **15.** $-48 + (-39) + 21$

16. On Friday, the low temperature was 12 degrees below zero. On Saturday, the low temperature was 6 degrees warmer. Write an expression to find Saturday's low temperature.

17. A fisherman has a baited hook 5 feet below the surface of the water. He does not catch any fish, so he lowers the hook 8 feet. He catches no fish there, so he raises the level of the hook 4 feet. How deep is the hook at this point?

In Exercises 18–21, find the sum.

18. $-34 + 52 + (-41) + (-7) + 11$ **19.** $78 + 39 + (-62) + (-46) + 11$

20. $-81 + (-57) + 69 + (-12) + 16$ **21.** $102 + 38 + (-89) + (-75) + 9$

22. Sarah owes $320 for the rent on her apartment. She also owes $45 for her electric bill and $57 for her phone bill. Her paycheck for this week is $415. Will her paycheck be enough to pay the bills? How much will be left over or how much will she still need?

Name _____ Date _____

Practice B
For use with pages 62–67

1. What addition problem does the number line show? What is the sum?

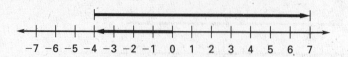

Use a number line to find the sum.

2. $5 + (-4)$ **3.** $-8 + 3$ **4.** $-2 + (-7)$

Find the sum.

5. $-54 + 63$ **6.** $29 + (-46)$ **7.** $-38 + (-59)$

8. $-93 + 86$ **9.** $12 + 38 + (-41)$ **10.** $-28 + 31 + (-44)$

11. $-101 + 95 + (-37)$ **12.** $53 + (-19) + (-102)$ **13.** $-98 + (-91) + 68$

Complete the statement using *always*, *sometimes*, or *never*.

14. The sum of two positive integers is _____ zero.

15. The sum of zero and a positive integer is _____ zero.

16. The sum of zero and a negative integer is _____ zero.

17. The sum of a positive integer and a negative integer is _____ zero.

In Exercises 18–21, find the sum.

18. $38 + 51 + (-29) + (-73)$ **19.** $-34 + (-85) + 63 + 47$

20. $102 + (-173) + 226 + (-185)$ **21.** $-304 + 246 + (-189) + 107$

22. Steven's bank account balance was $212 at the beginning of the month. He withdrew $63, $74, and $39. He also deposited $105 and $86. What was his balance after these transactions?

23. Yolanda was 8 seconds behind the leader after one lap of a two-mile track race. The same person led the race the whole way and won it. Here is how Yolanda lost or gained time on the leader in each of the remaining laps: lost 9 seconds, lost 3 seconds, gained 1 second, gained 2 seconds, gained 5 seconds, lost 3 seconds, gained 13 seconds. How many seconds behind the leader did Yolanda finish?

McDougal Littell Math, Course 3
Chapter 2   Resource Book

Name _____ Date _____

Practice C

For use with pages 62–67

Use a number line to find the sum.

1. $12 + (-8)$ **2.** $-16 + 9$ **3.** $-10 + (-7)$

Find the sum.

4. $24 + (-46)$ **5.** $-83 + 56$ **6.** $-37 + (-67)$

7. $-43 + 0 + 81$ **8.** $88 + (-91) + (-43)$ **9.** $-36 + 15 + (-28)$

10. $-32 + (-97) + (-37)$ **11.** $53 + (-27) + (-103)$ **12.** $-104 + (-125) + (-137)$

Complete the statement using *always*, *sometimes*, or *never*.

13. The sum of two integers is _____ positive.

14. The sum of two integers that are opposites is _____ zero.

15. The sum of the absolute values of two integers is _____ negative.

16. The sum of the absolute value of an integer and the opposite of the integer is _____ negative.

Find the sum.

17. $46 + 73 + (-38) + (-85)$ **18.** $-90 + (-67) + 74 + 82$

19. $105 + (-274) + 386 + (-259)$ **20.** $-461 + 289 + (-101) + 397$

In Exercises 21–24, evaluate $x + (-396)$ for the given value of x.

21. $x = 710$ **22.** $x = -841$ **23.** $x = |-563|$ **24.** $x = -|-992|$

25. In men's collegiate rowing, the average weight of each rower in an 8-person lightweight boat must be 155 pounds or less. The weights of each rower on a team, relative to this average, are: $+5, -3, -2, +2, -6, 0, -4, +5$ pounds. Does this team qualify?

In Exercises 26–29, solve the equation using mental math.

26. $-2 + m = 4$ **27.** $6 + j = 1$ **28.** $8 + h = -4$ **29.** $-3 = w + (-5)$

30. The Titanic shipwreck lies at a depth of 12,600 feet below sea level. Pikes Peak, in the Rocky Mountains, is 14,110 feet above sea level. Mt. Hood, in Oregon, is 11,239 feet above sea level. What is the difference in altitude of Pikes Peak and the Titanic wreckage? of Mt. Hood and the Titanic wreckage?

31. Does $|a + (-b)| = |a| + |-b|$ if a and b are both positive? What if a and b are both negative? What if a is positive and b is negative? What if a is negative and b is positive? Explain your answers.

LESSON 2.2

Study Guide

For use with pages 62–67

GOAL Add integers.

ADDING INTEGERS

To add integers with the **same sign,** add the absolute values and use the common sign.

To add integers with **different signs,** subtract the lesser absolute value from the greater absolute value. Use the sign of the number with the greater absolute value.

ADDITIVE IDENTITY PROPERTY

The sum of an integer and zero is the integer.

Algebra $a + 0 = a$

EXAMPLE 1 ## Adding Integers Using a Number Line

Use a number line to find the sum.

a. $9 + (-11)$ **b.** $-6 + 14$ **c.** $-3 + (-4)$

Solution

a. Start at 0, move **9** units to the right. Then move **11** units to the left.

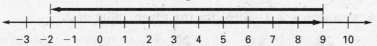

Answer: The final position is -2. So, $9 + (-11) = -2$.

b. Start at 0, move **6** units to the left. Then move **14** units to the right.

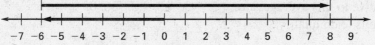

Answer: The final position is 8. So, $-6 + 14 = 8$.

c. Start at 0, move **3** units to the left. Then move **4** units to the left.

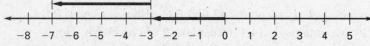

Answer: The final position is -7. So, $-3 + (-4) = -7$.

Exercises for Example 1

Use a number line to find the sum.

1. $2 + (-5)$ **2.** $-7 + (-6)$

3. $-8 + 5$ **4.** $-5 + 9$

LESSON 2.2 Continued

Study Guide

For use with pages 62–67

EXAMPLE 2 Adding Integers

Find the sum of $-11 + 8$.

$-11 + 8 = -3$ Different signs, so subtract $|8|$ from $|-11|$.
                         Use sign of number with greater absolute value.

Check   Use a number line to find the sum.

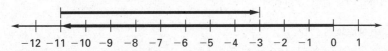

Exercises for Example 2

Find the sum.

5. $-19 + 18$ **6.** $-5 + 5$ **7.** $26 + (-32)$

EXAMPLE 3 Adding More Than Two Integers

a. Use the left to right rule of order of operations to find the sum.

$-15 + 0 + (-102) = -15 + (-102)$ Additive Identity Property

                       $= -117$ Same sign, sum has a common sign.

b. Use the left to right rule of order of operations to find the sum.

$-36 + (-26) + 56 = -62 + 56$ Same sign, sum has a common sign.

                   $= -$ Different signs, use sign of number with greater absolute value.

EXAMPLE 4 More Than Two Integers

On Monday, Maria has $125. The table shows her expenses and income for the week. How much money does Maria have on Friday?

Sweater	$-\$36$
CD	$-\$15$
Paycheck	$\$80$

Solution

First, add the positive integers, and then add the negative integers.

$125 + 80 + (-36) + (-15) = 205 + (-51)$

                               $= 154$

Answer: Maria has $154 on Friday.

Exercises for Examples 3 and 4

Find the sum.

8. $25 + (-23) + 4$ **9.** $-11 + 8 + (-14)$ **10.** $-56 + (-12) + 83$

11. $(-215) + (-125) + 832$ **12.** $525 + 154 + (-462)$ **13.** $-45 + 56 + (-45)$

Lesson 2.2

Name _____ Date _____

Quick Catch-Up for Absent Students

For use with pages 62–67

The items checked below were covered in class on (date missed) _____

Investigation 2.2: Adding Integers

_____ **Goal:** Model integer addition on a number line. (p. 62)

Lesson 2.2: Adding Integers

_____ **Goal:** Add integers. (pp. 63–65)

Material Covered:

_____ Example 1: Adding Integers Using a Number Line

_____ Guided Practice for Example 1

_____ Example 2: Adding Integers

_____ Example 3: Adding More Than Two Integers

_____ Example 4: Adding More Than Two Integers

_____ Another way

_____ Guided Practice for Examples 2, 3, and 4

Vocabulary:

    additive identity, p. 64   additive inverse, p. 64

_____ Other (specify)

_____

Homework and Additional Learning Support

_____ Textbook (specify) pp. 65–67

_____

_____ *Study Guide* worksheet (specify exercises)

_____ *@HomeTutor* for Lesson 2.2

Name _____ Date _____

Challenge Practice

For use with pages 62-67

Use mental math to find two different values of *x* that make the equation true.

1. $|x + 3| = 7$ **2.** $|x + (-4)| = 12$

3. $|x + (-5)| = 1$ **4.** $|10 + x| = 2$

5. $|-8 + x| = 10$ **6.** $|4 + x| = 9$

Translate the phrase into an expression. Simplify the expression.

7. 12 more than the sum of -4 and -6

8. The sum of -3 and 10, increased by 20

9. -2 added to the sum of -18 and 11

10. 14 added to the sum of -3, 5, and -12

Teacher's Name _____ Class _____ Room _____ Date_____

Teaching Guide

Key Concept

You can subtract an integer by adding its opposite.

Teaching the Lesson

Differentiating Instruction: See the Teacher's Edition side column notes on pages 70 and 71 and the notes on differentiating instruction in the *Course 3 Best Practices Toolkit*.

Teaching Notes and Suggested Questions: See the Teacher's Edition side column on page 69.

Activity Generator: See the Activity Generator Support Manual.

Animated Math: You may want to include the animation on page 71 in your lesson.

Starting the Lesson

Motivate the Lesson You can use subtraction of integers to find out how long it will take to pay back a debt. Use the information below to answer the questions at the right.

You borrow $175 from your aunt to buy a new CD player. You agree to pay her back by working at her house. You can earn at most $25 each day doing outside jobs and $20 each day doing inside jobs.

Alternative Lesson Starter

You may want to review prerequisite concepts, such as:

• integer (p. 57)

• opposite (p. 58)

• difference (p. 764)

Questions to Start the Lesson

1. Let the amount you owe your aunt be represented by 175. If you do only inside jobs, how much do you still owe your aunt after 1 day?

2. If you do only outside jobs, how much do you still owe your aunt after 3 days?

3. You decide to use $40 from your savings account in addition to doing an inside and an outside job each day. How many days will it take to back your aunt? (Find your answer using repeated subtraction.)

Common Student Errors

• When subtracting integers, students may write the opposite of the first number as well as the second number.

Example: Find the difference: $-6 - 5$.

Student answer: $-6 - 5 = 6 + (-5) = 1$

To subtract 5, add its opposite, which is -5. Therefore, $-6 - 5$ is equivalent to $-6 + (-5)$. The correct answer is -11.

Teaching Strategy of the Day

Teacher Preparation Extra minutes at the end of class should be used. Have questions prepared that you can ask students as a quick review of the day's lesson.

Teacher's Name _____ Class _____ Room _____ Date_____

Lesson Plan

Standard Schedule: 2 day lesson   Block Schedule: 1 day lesson

GOAL   **Subtract integers.**

State Standards _____

Focus and Motivate	**Starting Options**
	____ Homework Check (2.2): TE p. 66; Answer Transparencies
	____ Daily Homework Quiz (2.2): TE p. 67
	____ Warm-Up: Transparencies
	____ Starting the Lesson Questions: Teaching Guide
	____ Motivating the Lesson: TE p. 68
Teach	**Teaching Options**
	____ Alternative Lesson Openers: Electronic Classroom
	____ Classroom Activity: Activity Generator
	____ Examples 1–3: PE p. 69
	____ Extra Examples 1–3: TE p. 69
	____ Notetaking Guide pp. 28–29
	Checking for Understanding
	____ Closing the Lesson: TE p. 69
	____ Guided Practice Exercises: PE p. 69
Practice and Apply	**Assigning Homework**
	____ Basic: Day 1: pp. 70–72 Exs. 1–18, 36–37, 44, 48, 54–60; Day 2: EP p. 801 Exs. 14–16, pp. 70–72 Exs. 19–31, 40–43, 45–47, 49
	____ Average: Day 1: pp. 70–72 Exs. 1–18, 36–38*, 44, 48; Day 2: pp. 70–72 Exs. 19–35, 40–43, 45–47, 49–52, 54–60
	____ Advanced: Day 1: pp. 70–72 Exs. 1, 2, 4–18 even, 36–39*, 44, 48; Day 2: pp. 70–72 Exs. 19–35, 40, 43, 49–60*
	____ Block: pp. 70–72 Exs. 1–38, 40–52, 54–60
	____ Practice Masters: Chapter Resource Book pp. 27–29 (Levels A, B, or C)
Assess and Reteach	**Differentiating Instruction**
	____ Study Guide: Chapter Resource Book pp. 30–31
	____ Tutorial Software
	____ Challenge: Chapter Resource Book p. 31
	____ Remediation and Intervention Package: _____
	____ English Language Learners Package: _____
	Preparing for Standardized Tests
	____ Standardized Test Practice: PE pp. 70–72 Exs. 27, 36, 43, 47, 60
	Assessing the Lesson
	____ Daily Homework Quiz (2.3): TE p. 72 or Transparencies

LESSON 2.3 Activity Support Master

For use with page 68

Subtraction Problem	Difference	Addition Problem
$3 - 3$	0	$3 + (-3)$
$3 - 2$	____	$3 +$ ____
$3 - 1$	____	$3 +$ ____
$3 - 0$	____	$3 +$ ____
$3 - (-1)$	____	$3 +$ ____
$3 - (-2)$	____	$3 +$ ____
$3 - (-3)$	____	$3 +$ ____

Lesson 2.3

Name _____ Date _____

Practice A
For use with pages 68–72

Complete the equation.

1. $a - b =$ ____ + ____

2. $a - (-b) =$ ____ + ____

Match the expression with its answer.

3. $-7 - 12$ **A.** -18

4. $2 - 20$ **B.** -21

5. $-15 - 6$ **C.** 19

6. $13 - (-6)$ **D.** -19

Find the difference.

7. $4 - 7$ 8. $-2 - 5$ 9. $-3 - (-10)$

10. $-13 - 17$ 11. $18 - 15$ 12. $-12 - (-14)$

13. $-13 - (-13)$ 14. $-36 - (-21)$ 15. $16 - 38$

16. $25 - 42$ 17. $21 - 34$ 18. $-39 - (-46)$

Translate the verbal phrase into a numerical expression and simplify.

19. The difference of negative seven and twelve

20. The difference of thirteen and negative four

21. The difference of the opposite of nine and the opposite of fifteen

In Exercises 22–24, evaluate the expression when $a = -7$ and $b = 9$.

22. $12 - a - b$ 23. $a - 6 - b$ 24. $b - a - 4 - 8$

25. One day in Fairbanks, Alaska, the temperature is $-15°F$. During the night, the temperature drops by $16°F$. How cold does it get?

26. Because of a mistake in balancing her checkbook, Cora had a checking account balance of $-\$27$. Cora did not realize this and wrote another check for $\$34$. What is her balance now?

Evaluate the expression.

27. $37 - 206$ 28. $-319 + 187$ 29. $-645 - (-1238)$

30. $-7 - (-6) - (-5)$ 31. $-14 - 6 - (-9)$ 32. $6 - (-2) - 13$

33. $4 - (-11) - (-15)$ 34. $-31 - (-27) + (-43)$ 35. $26 + (-18) - 34$

LESSON 2.3 Practice B
For use with pages 68–72

Find the difference.

1. $7 - 11$ **2.** $-6 - 9$ **3.** $-5 - (-12)$

4. $-13 - 8$ **5.** $-16 - (-11)$ **6.** $15 - 18$

7. $23 - (-17)$ **8.** $21 - 35$ **9.** $-34 - (-18)$

10. $46 - 57$ **11.** $-61 - (-49)$ **12.** $-37 - 58$

Translate the verbal phrase into a numerical expression and simplify.

13. The difference of a negative six and nineteen

14. The difference of eight and negative twenty-one

15. The difference of the opposite of fifteen and the opposite of twenty-eight

Evaluate the expression when $x = -8$ and $y = 5$.

16. $7 - x - y$ **17.** $x - 15 - y$ **18.** $x - y - 4 - 12$

19. Jose's credit card statement says that he owes $324. He charges an additional $63, $21, and $75. How much does he owe now?

20. A scuba diver is 31 feet below the surface of the water. She dives down an additional 16 feet. How far would she have to rise to reach the surface of the water?

Evaluate the expression.

21. $57 - 304$ **22.** $-568 + 493$ **23.** $-219 - (-1065)$

24. $-8 - (-4) - (-7)$ **25.** $-16 - 10 - (-14)$ **26.** $63 - 48 - 39$

27. $-34 - (-15) - (-18)$ **28.** $37 - (-41) - 86$ **29.** $-54 - 81 - (-47)$

In Exercises 30–35, evaluate the expression when $a = -5$, $b = 12$, and $c = -8$.

30. $a - b - 14$ **31.** $b - c + a$ **32.** $b - 11 - c$

33. $c - 7 - a$ **34.** $c - 16 + b$ **35.** $a - b - c$

36. Which of the temperature changes represents the greatest temperature drop in degrees?

   a. From 16°F down to −21°F   **b.** From −4°F down to −39°F

   c. From 33°F down to −6°F   **d.** From −14°F down to −54°F

37. The values below show the daily change (in cents) in the value of one share of stock.

$-17, -7, +3, -8, +12, -21, -33, +34, -11, -19$

What was the total change in the value of the stock over the 10 days?

Name _____ Date _____

Practice C

For use with pages 68–72

Find the difference.

1. $4 - 12$
2. $-8 - 19$
3. $-7 - (-11)$
4. $-13 - 15$
5. $-17 - (-19)$
6. $-23 - (-41)$
7. $38 - 46$
8. $29 - (-35)$
9. $-47 - (-53)$
10. $-37 - 43$
11. $56 - 69$
12. $-82 - (-51)$

Translate the verbal phrase into a numerical expression and simplify.

13. The difference of sixteen and negative twenty-four

14. The difference of the opposite of twenty-six and the opposite of thirty-one

In Exercises 15–17, evaluate the expression when $m = -11$ and $p = 9$.

15. $m - p - 4$
16. $p - m - 8$
17. $m - p - 14 - 23$

18. Explain how you can find the distance between the points on the number line using subtraction.

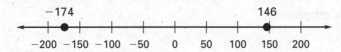

Use the table at the right showing the position relative to sea level of several aquatic mammals during their deepest dives.

19. How much deeper can a Bottlenose Dolphin dive than a Pacific White-Sided Dolphin?

20. How much deeper can a Pilot Whale dive than a Dall's Porpoise?

21. If you could combine the maximum dives of a Dall's Porpoise and a Beluga Whale, how close would it be to the maximum dive of a Pilot Whale?

Animal	Position
Dall's Porpoise	-330 ft
Pacific White-Sided Dolphin	-660 ft
Beluga Whale	-990 ft
Bottlenose Dolphin	-1640 ft
Pilot Whale	-1970 ft

Evaluate the expression.

22. $98 - 465$
23. $-391 + 408$
24. $-806 - (-1239)$
25. $-9 - (-7) - (-13)$
26. $-23 - 16 - (-19)$
27. $-71 - 65 - 94$
28. $-84 - (-37) - (-43)$
29. $-106 - (-97) - 45$
30. $139 - 152 - 206$

Evaluate the expression when $x = -11$, $y = 17$, and $z = -24$.

31. $x - y - 21$
32. $y - z + x$
33. $y - 36 - z$

Lesson 2.3

LESSON 2.3

Study Guide

For use with pages 68–72

GOAL Subtract integers.

SUBTRACTING INTEGERS

To subtract an integer, add its opposite.

Algebra $a - b = a + (-b)$

$a - (-b) = a + b$

EXAMPLE 1 Subtracting Integers

a. $-25 - (-8) = -25 + 8$ Add the opposite of -8.

$= -17$ Add the integers.

b. $-18 - 35 = -18 + (-35)$ Add the opposite of 35.

$= -53$ Add the integers.

Exercises for Example 1

Find the difference.

1. $26 - 32$

2. $-9 - 16$

3. $36 - (-36)$

4. $-12 - (-52)$

5. $-78 - 45$

6. $85 - (-2)$

7. $46 - 49$

8. $-8 - 34$

EXAMPLE 2 Evaluating Variable Expressions

Evaluate $a - (-b) - 16$ when $a = 21$ and $b = 4$.

Solution

$a - (-b) - 16 = 21 - (-4) - 16$ Substitute 21 for a and 4 for b.

$= 21 + 4 - 16$ Add the opposite of -4.

$= 21 + 4 + (-16)$ Add the opposite of 16.

$= 9$ Add the integers.

Exercises for Example 2

Evaluate the expression when $x = 11$ and $y = -7$.

9. $9 - x$

10. $-8 - y$

11. $y - x$

12. $x - y$

13. $16 - x - y$

14. $y + 17 - x$

Lesson 2.3

Name _____ Date _____

Study Guide
For use with pages 68–72

EXAMPLE 3 **Using Integer Subtraction**

A football team gained 3 yards, lost 1 yard, gained 10 yards, lost 8 yards, and then lost 11 yards. Find the net gain or loss.

Solution

The net gain or loss is the sum or difference of the yards gained or lost.

Net gain or loss $= 3 - 1 + 10 - 8 - 11$	Write a statement of yards gained or lost.
$= 3 + (-1) + 10 + (-8) + (-11)$	Add the opposite of 1, 8, and 11.
$= -7$	Add the integers.

Because the answer is a negative number, the value represents a loss.

Answer: The football team lost 7 yards.

Exercises for Example 3

15. You borrow $34 then pay back $16. How much money do you owe?

16. Jacob opens a bank account with a deposit of $156. He writes 3 checks for $15, $78, and $56. How much money does he have now in his bank account?

LESSON 2.3 Quick Catch-Up for Absent Students

For use with pages 68–72

The items checked below were covered in class on (date missed) _____

Lesson 2.3: Subtracting integers

____ **Goal:** Subtract integers. (pp. 68–69)

Material Covered:

____ Example 1: Subtracting Integers

____ Example 2: Evaluating a Variable Expression

____ Example 3: Standardized Test Practice

____ Eliminate choices

____ Guided Practice for Examples 1, 2, and 3

____ Other (specify)

_____

Homework and Additional Learning Support

____ Textbook (specify) pp. 70–72

_____

____ *Study Guide* worksheet (specify exercises)

____ *@HomeTutor* for Lesson 2.3

Lesson 2.3

Name _____ Date _____

Challenge Practice

For use with pages 68–72

Use mental math to find two different values of *x* that make the equation true.

1. $|x - 6| = 4$

2. $|x - 2| = 1$

3. $|9 - x| = 15$

4. $|4 - x| = 10$

In Exercises 5–7, let *x* represent a positive integer and *y* represent a negative integer. Tell whether the expression must be positive or negative.

5. $x - y$

6. $y - x$

7. $-|-x|$

In Exercises 8–10, use the statement $|x - y| = |x| - |y|$.

8. Name a pair of values for *x* and *y* that makes the statement false.

9. Name two different pairs of values for *x* and *y* that make the statement true.

10. Is the statement true if *x* and *y* are both positive and *x* is greater than *y*?
What if *x* and *y* are both positive and *x* is less than *y*?

LESSON 2.4 Teaching Guide

Key Concept

The product of two integers with the same sign is positive. The product of two integers with different signs is negative.

Teaching the Lesson

Differentiating Instruction: See the Teacher's Edition side column notes on page 75 and the notes on differentiating instruction in the *Course 3 Best Practices Toolkit*.

Teaching Notes and Suggested Questions: See the Teacher's Edition side columns on page 74.

Activity Generator: See the Activity Generator Support Manual.

Animated Math: You may want to include the animation on page 74 in your lesson.

Starting the Lesson

Motivate the Lesson You can use integer multiplication to find the cost of items at a store. Use the information below to answer the questions at the right.

At an electronics store, you buy 4 CDs that cost $12 each and 3 DVDs that cost $18 each.

Alternative Lesson Starter

You may want to review prerequisite concepts, such as:

- integer (p. 57)
- product (p. 768)

Questions to Start the Lesson

1. How much do 4 CDs cost?

2. How much do 3 DVDs cost?

3. What is the total cost of the items you bought at the electronics store?

4. Suppose the electronics store is having a sale in which each CD is $3 off and each DVD is $5 off. What would be the total cost of items you bought at the electronics store?

Common Student Errors

Tip Students will find the rules for multiplication easier to learn than those for integer addition and subtraction.

Tip Remind students that when working with variables, multiplication is understood when two or more variables are written without an operation symbol between them.

Example: Evaluate $xy - 5y$ when $x = 6$ and $y = -4$.

Students answer: $xy - 5y = 6(-4) - 5(-4)$
$$= 2 - 1$$
$$= 1$$

You multiply 6 by -4 and 5 by -4. You do not subtract 4 from 6 or 4 from 5. The correct answer is -4.

Teaching Strategy of the Day

Motivating Students Start class when the bell rings. Engaging the class in the Lesson Starter, a homework problem, or an activity motivates all students to focus on the topic.

Teacher's Name _____ Class _____ Room _____ Date_____

Lesson Plan

Standard Schedule: 2 day lesson   Block Schedule: 1 day lesson

GOAL   **Multiply integers.**

State Standards _____

Focus and Motivate	**Starting Options**
	____ Homework Check (2.3): TE p. 70; Answer Transparencies
	____ Daily Homework Quiz (2.3): TE p. 72
	____ Warm-Up: Transparencies
	____ Starting the Lesson Questions: Teaching Guide
	____ Motivating the Lesson: TE p. 73

Teach

Teaching Options

____ Alternative Lesson Openers: Electronic Classroom

____ Classroom Activity: Activity Generator; Chapter Resource Book p. 37

____ Examples 1–3: PE pp. 73–74

____ Extra Examples 1–3: TE p. 74

____ Notetaking Guide pp. 30–32

Checking for Understanding

____ Closing the Lesson: TE p. 74

____ Guided Practice Exercises: PE pp. 74

Practice and Apply

Assigning Homework

____ Basic: Day 1: pp. 75–76 Exs. 1–23, 36–40, 53, 54, 57–59, 62–66;
Day 2: SRH p. 792 Exs. 1–10, pp. 75–76 Exs. 24–35, 41–44, 55, 56

____ Average: Day 1: pp. 75–76 Exs. 1, 2, 4–22 even, 23, 36–40, 49, 50*, 57–60;
Day 2: pp. 75–76 Exs. 24–35, 41–44, 56, 62–66

____ Advanced: Day 1: pp. 75–76 Exs. 1, 2, 23, 36–40, 49–52*, 57–61*;
Day 2: pp. 75–76 Exs. 24–35, 41–48, 56, 66

____ Block: pp. 75–76 Exs. 1, 2, 4–22 even, 23–44, 49, 50*, 56–60, 62–66

____ Practice Masters: Chapter Resource Book pp. 39–41 (Levels A, B, or C)

Assess and Reteach

Differentiating Instruction

____ Study Guide: Chapter Resource Book pp. 42–43

____ Tutorial Software

____ Challenge: Chapter Resource Book p. 45

____ Remediation and Intervention Package: _____

____ English Language Learners Package: _____

Preparing for Standardized Tests

____ Standardized Test Practice: PE pp. 75–76 Exs. 40, 56, 58, 59, 66

Assessing the Lesson

____ Daily Homework Quiz (2.4): TE p. 76 or Transparencies

LESSON 2.4

Activity Master
For use before Lesson 2.4

Goal	Materials
Use patterns to multiply two integers.	• paper • pencil

Evaluating The Product of Two Integers

In this activity, you will use patterns to evaluate the sign of the product of two integers.

EXPLORE **Use the pattern of the products to complete the table.**
Notice that the products decrease by 3. So,
$3 \cdot 0 = 0$, $3 \cdot (-1) = -3$, and $3 \cdot (-2) = -6$.

Expression	Product
$3 \cdot 3$	9
$3 \cdot 2$	6
$3 \cdot 1$	3
$3 \cdot 0$	___
$3 \cdot (-1)$	___
$3 \cdot (-2)$	___

Your turn now

1. What can you say about the product of a positive integer and a negative integer?

Find the product.

2. $3(-3)$ 3. $3(-4)$ 4. $-3(5)$ 5. $-3(6)$

6. Use your conclusion in Exercise 1 to complete the first three rows of the table at the right. Look for a pattern in the products. Use the pattern to complete the table.

Expression	Product
$3 \cdot (-2)$	___
$2 \cdot (-2)$	___
$1 \cdot (-2)$	___
$0 \cdot (-2)$	___
$-1 \cdot (-2)$	___
$-2 \cdot (-2)$	___

7. Use the table in Exercise 6 to describe the product of two negative integers.

Name _____ Date _____

Technology Keystrokes

For use with Exercise 56, page 76

TI-34 II

56. [(-)] 16 [×] 1 [x^2] [+] 100 [ENTER =]

[(-)] 16 [×] 2 [x^2] [+] 100 [ENTER =]

[(-)] 16 [×] 3 [x^2] [+] 100 [ENTER =]

TI-73

56. [(-)] 16 [×] 1 [x^2] [+] 100 [ENTER]

[(-)] 16 [×] 2 [x^2] [+] 100 [ENTER]

[(-)] 16 [×] 3 [x^2] [+] 100 [ENTER]

Name _____ Date _____

Practice A

For use with pages 73–76

Match the expression with its answer.

1. $5(-8)$ **A.** 48

2. $-4(-10)$ **B.** 40

3. $8(-6)$ **C.** -40

4. $-3(-16)$ **D.** -48

Find the product.

5. $3(-8)$ 6. $-7(-6)$ 7. $0(-14)$

8. $5(-10)$ 9. $-11(-3)$ 10. $-12(-13)$

11. $-14(7)$ 12. $8(-19)$ 13. $-15(16)$

14. $-2(4)(-8)$ 15. $6(-8)(-9)$ 16. $-7(-7)(-3)$

Evaluate the expression when $x = -8$, $y = -5$, and $z = -3$.

17. $4xy$ 18. $7xz$ 19. $xy - z$

20. $zy + x$ 21. $9xyz$ 22. $-3xy + 2zx$

Find the product.

23. $|-7| \cdot 3$ 24. $-6 \cdot |15|$ 25. $-3(-9) \cdot |-5|$

In Exercises 26–28, use mental math to solve the equation.

26. $4x = -20$ 27. $-5x = -35$ 28. $-2(3)x = 42$

29. You were carrying $45 in your pocket, but three $5 bills slipped out and you lost them. How much money do you have now?

30. A person planted 8 rows of 9 tomato plants in a vegetable garden. Heavy rains washed 3 of the rows out. The rest of the plants all yielded tomatoes. How many of the tomato plants yielded tomatoes?

31. Marie has $400 in a savings account. She withdraws $30 each week for six weeks to pay for piano lessons. How much money is left in her savings account?

32. A man goes on a diet and loses 3 pounds a month for 8 months. What is the total change in the man's weight?

LESSON 2.4

Practice B
For use with pages 73–76

Find the product.

1. $4(-9)$　　　　　　**2.** $-5(-7)$　　　　　　**3.** $-12(0)$

4. $-9(-11)$　　　　　**5.** $-12(8)$　　　　　　**6.** $-13(-20)$

7. $-17(18)$　　　　　**8.** $-4(-9)(8)$　　　　**9.** $6(-5)(7)$

10. $-9(-8)(11)$　　　**11.** $42(-3)(0)$　　　　**12.** $-5(-7)(-13)$

Evaluate the expression when $x = -9$, $y = -7$, and $z = -11$.

13. $2xy$　　　　　　　**14.** $-6yz$　　　　　　**15.** $yz - 4x$

16. $xy + 3z$　　　　　**17.** $7xyz$　　　　　　**18.** $5xy - 7zx$

Find the product.

19. $|-12| \cdot 4$　　　　**20.** $-7 \cdot |9|$　　　　　**21.** $-4(-8) \cdot |-5|$

In Exercises 22–24, use mental math to solve the equation.

22. $3x = -21$　　　　**23.** $-12x = -36$　　　　**24.** $-3(5)x = 75$

25. A roofing contractor has 29 bundles of roofing shingles that he needs to carry up a ladder and put onto a roof. He carries two bundles at a time. How many bundles are still on the ground after his seventh trip up the ladder?

26. A football team starts with the ball at their own 20-yard line. They make two 6-yard gains in a row, then they have three 5-yard losses in a row. What yard line is the ball on at this point?

In Exercises 27–29, evaluate the expression when $x = -6$ and $y = -13$.

27. $-x(y)$　　　　　　**28.** $x(y^2)(x)$　　　　　**29.** $[y + (-x)(y)]^2$

30. There is an old saying that goes, "Every time I go one step forward, I get bumped two steps backward." Taken literally, what would the person's forward progress be after going through this process 23 times?

31. You went to the department store for back to school shopping and picked out 6 shirts and 4 pairs of pants with a total worth of $170. When you paid for the clothes, the cashier took $3 off the price of each shirt and $5 off the price of each pair of pants. There was no sales tax. How much did you have to pay?

Lesson 2.4

Name _____ Date _____

Practice C

For use with pages 73–76

Find the product.

1. $5(-9)$

2. $-11(-7)$

3. $-18(0)$

4. $8(-15)$

5. $14(-16)$

6. $-15(-19)$

7. $-21(23)$

8. $-8(-4)(-3)$

9. $12(-7)(-5)$

10. $9(-13)(10)$

11. $43(-17)(0)$

12. $-16(8)(-7)$

Evaluate the expression when $x = -11$, $y = -13$, and $z = -16$.

13. $8xy$

14. $-7yz$

15. $yz - 5x$

16. $xy + 5z$

17. $-3xyz$

18. $4xz - 9yx$

Find the product.

19. $|-15| \cdot 7$

20. $-6 \cdot |12|$

21. $-3(-9) \cdot |11|$

In Exercises 22–24, use mental math to solve the equation.

22. $6x = -48$

23. $-13x = -39$

24. $-4(6)x = 48$

25. Carol has a balance of $520 in her checking account. She writes three checks each for $120 from the account. She also deposits 2 paychecks for $240 each. What is her balance now?

26. A new car dealer is running a sale. Retail prices of all sedans are discounted by $1500, all sports cars by $2500, and all sport utility vehicles by $3000. There are 8 sports cars, 7 sedans, and 11 sport utility vehicles on the lot. The cars have a total retail value of $650,000. What is the total of the prices of all of the cars after the discounts are applied?

In Exercises 27–32, evaluate the expression when $x = -21$, $y = -36$, and $z = 42$.

27. $-x(y)(z)$

28. $x(y^2) - (-x)z$

29. $\left[zx + xy\right]^2$

30. $xz - xyz$

31. $4yz + xy$

32. $-3zx - 5yz$

33. What is the value of n in the expression $an = -a$?

34. What is the value of a in the expression $24c + 15b + 11a = 24c + 15b$?

35. What is the value of x in the expression $x^7 = -1$?

36. What must be true about n in the expression $(-1)^n = -1$?

37. What must be true about the value of n in the expression $(-1)^n = 1$?

Study Guide

For use with pages 73–76

GOAL Multiply integers.

MULTIPLYING INTEGERS

The product of two integers with the same sign is positive.

The product of two integers with different signs is negative.

MULTIPLICATION PROPERTIES

Multiplication Property of Zero

The product of an integer and 0 is 0.

Identity Property of Multiplication

The product of an integer and 1 is the integer.

EXAMPLE 1 Multiplying Integers

Suppose you travel at a rate of 55 miles per hour for 4 hours. Use the formula $d = rt$ to find your distance traveled.

$$d = rt \qquad \text{Write the distance formula.}$$
$$d = 55 \cdot 4 \qquad \text{Substitute 55 for } r \text{ and 4 for } t.$$
$$d = 220 \qquad \text{Same signs, so product is positive.}$$

Answer: The distance traveled is 220 miles.

Exercises for Example 1

1. Find the distance traveled if you travel at a rate of 50 miles per hour for 2 hours.

2. You have $300 in a savings account. Over a 1-month period, you make 5 withdrawals of $15 each. What is your new balance?

Study Guide

For use with pages 73–76

EXAMPLE 2 ## Multiplying Two or More Integers

a. $-8(9) = -72$	Different signs, so product is negative.
b. $-12(-11) = 132$	Same sign, so product is positive.
c. $-24(1) = -24$	Product of a number and 1 is the number.
d. $-9(-4)(-3) = 36(-3)$	Multiply using left to right rule.
$\qquad = -108$	Multiply.

Exercises for Example 2

Find the product.

3. $-5(6)$ **4.** $-12(-1)$

5. $-7(-11)$ **6.** $-5(0)$

7. $-3(2)(-4)$ **8.** $5(68)(0)$

9. $-16(-1)(-3)$ **10.** $7(-2)(4)$

EXAMPLE 3 ## Evaluating Variable Expressions with Integers

Evaluate $2a - b^2$ when $a = -12$ and $b = -4$.

$2a - b^2 = 2(-12) - (-4)^2$	Substitute -12 for a and -4 for b.
$\qquad = 2(-12) - (16)$	Evaluate the power.
$\qquad = -24 - 16$	Multiply 2 and -12.
$\qquad = -24 + (-16)$	Add the opposite of 16.
$\qquad = -40$	Add.

Exercises for Example 3

Evaluate the expression when $a = -2$, $b = -1$, and $c = 5$.

11. $a - bc$ **12.** $ac - b$

13. $b - a^2$ **14.** $ab - c^2$

Name _____ Date _____

Quick Catch-Up for Absent Students
For use with pages 73–76

The items checked below were covered in class on (date missed) _____

Lesson 2.4: Multiplying Integers

____ **Goal:** Multiply integers. (pp. 73–74)

Material Covered:

____ Example 1: Multiplying Integers

____ Example 2: Multiplying Two or More Integers

____ Avoid errors

____ Example 3: Evaluating an Expression with Integers

____ Guided Practice for Examples 1, 2, and 3

Vocabulary:

multiplicative inverse, p. 74

____ Other (specify)

_____

Homework and Additional Learning Support

____ Textbook (specify) pp. 75–76

_____

____ *Study Guide* worksheet (specify exercises)

____ @*HomeTutor* for Lesson 2.4

Lesson 2.4

Name _____ Date _____

Challenge Practice

For use with pages 73–76

In Exercises 1–4, use the strategy *look for a pattern* and the table below.

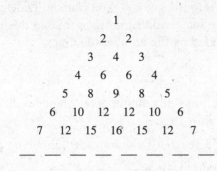

```
              1
           2     2
        3     4     3
     4     6     6     4
  5     8     9     8     5
6    10    12    12    10    6
7   12   15   16   15   12   7
__ __ __ __ __ __ __ __
  __ __ __ __ __ __ __ __ __
```

1. Complete rows 8 and 9 in the table above.

2. How many terms are in the 6th row? the 9th row? the nth row?

3. List the numbers in the middle of each odd-numbered row. What will the middle number be in the 11th row? the 13th row?

4. List the terms in the 14th row without completing rows 10 through 13. (*Hint:* Look for patterns in the rows and diagonals in the triangle.)

In Exercises 5–7, complete the statement with < or > without multiplying the numbers.

5. $(-5)^4$ ____ $(-5)^3$

6. $(-1)^{15}$ ____ $(-1)^8$

7. $(-15)(-34)(-78)$ ____ $(-15)(34)(-78)$

LESSON 2.5

Teaching Guide

Key Concept

The quotient of two integers with the same sign is positive. The quotient of two integers with different signs is negative. The quotient of zero and any nonzero integer is 0. You cannot divide a number by 0. Any number divided by 0 is undefined. You will use integer division when finding the mean of a data. The mean of a data set is the sum of the values divided by the number of values.

Teaching the Lesson

Differentiating Instruction: See the Teacher's Edition side column notes on pages 79 and 80 and the notes on differentiating instruction in the *Course 3 Best Practices Toolkit.*

Teaching Notes and Suggested Questions: See the Teacher's Edition side column on page 78.

Activity Generator: See the Activity Generator Support Manual.

Starting the Lesson

Motivate the Lesson You can use integer division to find an average weekly shopping cost. Use the information below to answer the questions at the right.

A family shops for groceries weekly. Over a two month period, the family's grocery bills are $85, $77, $98, $118, $84, $75, $90, and $93.

Alternative Lesson Starter

You can also introduce the concept of integer division by using temperature or elevation.

Questions to Start the Lesson

1. Add the grocery bills for the two month period.

2. How many weeks has the family shopped for groceries?

3. What is the average weekly cost for groceries over this two month period?

4. The family spends $72 on groceries the next week. Without performing any calculations, how will this affect the average weekly cost?

Common Student Errors

- If students know the rules for multiplying integers, then they should easily learn the rules for dividing integers. The rules for dividing integers are similar to the rules for multiplying integers.

  Tip Remind students that you *cannot* divide a number by 0, but you *can* divide 0 by a number.

Example: Find the quotient: $\frac{0}{6}$.

Student answer: undefined

The correct answer is 0.

Teaching Strategy of the Day

Asking Questions Avoid negative reactions (facial expressions, body language, and so on) when a student gives a wrong answer. A student that has given an answer has tried. You want the student to be willing to continue to answer and ask questions during class.

LESSON
2.5
Continued

Teacher's Name _____ Class _____ Room _____ Date _____

Lesson Plan

Standard Schedule: 1 day lesson   Block Schedule: 0.5 day lesson with 2.6

GOAL   **Divide integers.**

State Standards _____

Focus and Motivate	**Starting Options**
	____ Homework Check (2.4): TE p. 75; Answer Transparencies
	____ Daily Homework Quiz (2.4): TE p. 76
	____ Warm-Up: Transparencies
	____ Starting the Lesson Questions: Teaching Guide
	____ Motivating the Lesson: TE p. 77
Teach	**Teaching Options**
	____ Alternative Lesson Openers: Electronic Classroom
	____ Classroom Activity: Activity Generator
	____ Examples 1–3: PE pp. 77–78
	____ Extra Examples 1–3: TE p. 78
	____ Problem Solving: Mixed Problem Solving: Chapter Resource Book p. 55
	____ Real World Problem Solving: Chapter Resource Book p. 56
	____ Notetaking Guide pp. 33–35
	Checking for Understanding
	____ Closing the Lesson: TE p. 78
	____ Guided Practice Exercises: PE pp. 77–78
Practice and Apply	**Assigning Homework**
	____ Basic: Day 1: pp. 79–81 Exs. 1, 2–20 even, 26–29, 34, 36, 38–44, 48–54
	____ Average: Day 1: pp. 79–81 Exs. 1, 2–36 even, 38–44, 48–54
	____ Advanced: Day 1: pp. 79–81 Exs. 1, 18–41*, 44–47*, 54
	____ Block: pp. 79–81 Exs. 1, 2–36 even, 38–44, 48–54 (with 2.6)
	____ Practice Masters: Chapter Resource Book pp. 49–51 (Levels A, B, or C)
Assess and Reteach	**Differentiating Instruction**
	____ Study Guide: Chapter Resource Book pp. 52–53
	____ Tutorial Software
	____ Challenge: Chapter Resource Book p. 57
	____ Remediation and Intervention Package: _____
	____ English Language Learners Package: _____
	Preparing for Standardized Tests
	____ Standardized Test Practice: PE pp. 79–81 Exs. 35, 39, 40, 41, 54
	Assessing the Lesson
	____ Daily Homework Quiz (2.5): TE p. 81 or Transparencies

LESSON

2.5

Technology Keystrokes

For use with Exercise 39, page 80

TI-34 II

39. (400 + (-) 76 + (-) 139 +
526 + 650 + (-) 17) ÷ 6 ENTER

TI-73

39. (400 + (-) 76 + (-) 139 +
526 + 650 + (-) 17) ÷ 6 ENTER

Name _____ Date _____

Practice A
For use with pages 77–81

Tell whether the statement is *true* or *false*.

1. The quotient of two integers with the same sign is negative.

2. The quotient of two integers with different signs is negative.

3. The quotient of zero and any nonzero integer is zero.

4. The mean of a set of data is the number of items in the set of data divided by the sum of the numbers in the set.

Find the quotient.

5. $\dfrac{-35}{7}$

6. $\dfrac{-63}{-9}$

7. $\dfrac{-21}{3}$

8. $\dfrac{40}{-8}$

9. $\dfrac{0}{16}$

10. $\dfrac{-72}{9}$

11. $\dfrac{-12}{3}$

12. $\dfrac{-24}{-6}$

13. $\dfrac{45}{5}$

14. $\dfrac{-46}{0}$

15. $\dfrac{-33}{11}$

16. $\dfrac{64}{-8}$

Evaluate the expression when $x = 16$, $y = -4$, and $z = -8$.

17. $\dfrac{x}{z}$

18. $\dfrac{x}{y}$

19. $\dfrac{x}{(z - y)}$

20. $\dfrac{(z - x)}{y}$

21. $\dfrac{z^2}{y}$

22. $\dfrac{2z}{y}$

In Exercises 23–26, find the mean of the data.

23. $7, -6, 8, -10, -8, 4, 5$

24. $-5, -4, -7, -8, 1, 2, -6, 3$

25. $-2, 10, -15, -7, 4, 8$

26. $-8, 7, 4, 2, -3, 9, 3$

27. One winter, the low temperatures for five consecutive days in Buffalo, New York were $-5°F$, $-8°F$, $-12°F$, $-9°F$, and $-6°F$. What was the mean low temperature in Buffalo over the five days?

28. There were 6 eighth graders on a middle school wrestling team. The changes in weights for the 6 wrestlers from the first day of practice to the end of the season were $+3$ pounds, -2 pounds, -1 pound, -4 pounds, $+2$ pounds, and -4 pounds. Find the mean weight change of these wrestlers.

LESSON 2.5

Practice B

For use with pages 77–81

Find the quotient.

1. $\dfrac{-64}{-8}$

2. $\dfrac{-32}{4}$

3. $\dfrac{50}{-10}$

4. $\dfrac{0}{-29}$

5. $\dfrac{-65}{0}$

6. $\dfrac{-36}{3}$

7. $\dfrac{30}{-15}$

8. $\dfrac{56}{-7}$

9. $\dfrac{-36}{4}$

10. $\dfrac{-48}{-6}$

11. $\dfrac{42}{-2}$

12. $\dfrac{-60}{-12}$

Evaluate the expression when $a = -24$, $b = -6$, and $c = -12$.

13. $\dfrac{a}{b}$

14. $\dfrac{bc}{a}$

15. $\dfrac{-c}{b}$

16. $\dfrac{ac}{b}$

17. $\dfrac{c^2}{a}$

18. $\dfrac{(a + c)}{b}$

Find the mean of the data.

19. $8, 5, -4, 9, -3, 11, 2$

20. $-7, -13, 5, 2, -8, -9$

21. $-16, 2, -18, 4, -11, -8, -6, 5$

22. $-4, 11, -6, 14, -3, 7, 2$

Use the table at the right, showing the final golf scores, relative to par, of the top eleven golfers at the 2001 Masters Tournament.

23. Calculate the mean score of the golfers.

24. Par for the tournament was 288 strokes. Find the actual number of strokes taken by each of the golfers. For example, to find Tiger Wood's number of strokes, subtract $288 - 12$. So, Woods took 276 strokes in the tournament.

25. What is the *mean* number of strokes taken in the tournament by the 11 golfers?

26. Convert the average score against par found in Exercise 23 to a number of strokes. How does the number compare with the average you found in Exercise 25?

Player	Final
T. Woods	−12
R. Goosen	−9
P. Mickelson	−8
J. Olazabal	−7
P. Harrington	−6
E. Els	−6
V. Singh	−5
S. Garcia	−4
M. Jimenez	−3
A. Scott	−3
A. Cabrera	−3

LESSON 2.5

Practice C
For use with pages 77–81

Find the quotient.

1. $\dfrac{-32}{8}$ **2.** $\dfrac{-63}{-9}$ **3.** $\dfrac{42}{-7}$

4. $\dfrac{-45}{3}$ **5.** $\dfrac{-66}{11}$ **6.** $\dfrac{96}{-8}$

7. $\dfrac{0}{-15}$ **8.** $\dfrac{-108}{-12}$ **9.** $\dfrac{-35}{0}$

10. $\dfrac{-86}{-2}$ **11.** $\dfrac{164}{-4}$ **12.** $\dfrac{-135}{-9}$

Evaluate the expression when $m = -48$, $n = -8$, and $p = -16$.

13. $\dfrac{m}{p}$ **14.** $\dfrac{m^2}{n}$ **15.** $\dfrac{mp}{n}$

16. $\dfrac{(m-p)}{n}$ **17.** $\dfrac{p^2}{n}$ **18.** $\dfrac{m}{(n+p)}$

Find the mean of the data.

19. $7, -2, -9, 2, 11, 6, 4, -3$

20. $15, -13, -21, 4, 19, -16, -7, -5$

21. $-4, -6, -5, 2, 19, -53, -21, -12, 6, 4$

22. $23, -4, -7, 15, 3, 9, -4, 9, 1$

In Exercises 23–25, find the quotient.

23. $\dfrac{-12}{5}$ **24.** $\dfrac{-18}{-15}$ **25.** $\dfrac{4}{-64}$

26. In football, when the quarterback is tackled behind the line of scrimmage on a pass play, it counts as a rush with negative yardage. In one game, a quarterback had rushes of $-8, 2, 7, -18, -9, 0, -6, 5, -2$, and -3 yards. What was the mean number of yards per rush?

27. A paper mill that had employed a large number of the people who lived nearby closed. There were 6 members of one family employed at the mill. All of them had to find other jobs. The amounts below represent the changes in yearly income of the family members after finding different jobs. Find the mean change in yearly income.

$-\$2600, \$1200, -\$5200, -\$8000, \$5600, -\$7200$

Name _____ Date _____

Study Guide

For use with pages 77–81

GOAL Divide integers.

DIVIDING INTEGERS

The quotient of two integers with the same sign is positive.

The quotient of two integers with different signs is negative.

The quotient of zero and any nonzero integer is 0.

VOCABULARY

A **mean,** also called the *average,* is the sum of the numbers in a set of data divided by the number of items in the set.

EXAMPLE 1 **Dividing Integers**

a. $\dfrac{-36}{-12} = 3$ Same sign, so quotient is positive.

b. $\dfrac{-56}{8} = -7$ Different signs, so quotient is negative.

c. $\dfrac{45}{-9} = -5$ Different signs, so quotient is negative.

d. $\dfrac{0}{-18} = 0$ The quotient of zero and any nonzero integer is 0.

Exercises for Example 1

Find the quotient.

1. $\dfrac{-58}{-1}$ 2. $\dfrac{38}{-2}$ 3. $\dfrac{-72}{6}$

4. $\dfrac{200}{-25}$ 5. $\dfrac{0}{-9}$ 6. $\dfrac{37}{-37}$

McDougal Littell Math, Course 3
Chapter 2   Resource Book

Name _____ Date _____

Study Guide

For use with pages 77–81

EXAMPLE 2 **Finding a Mean**

Find the mean of the data.

$21, -56, -46, 32, -14$

$21 + (-56) + (-46) + 32 + (-14) = -63$ Find the sum.

$$\frac{-63}{5} = -12.6$$ Divide the sum by the number of data values.

Answer: The mean of the data is -12.6.

Exercises for Example 2

Find the mean of the data.

7. $11, 9, 6, 7, 8, 8, 13, 10$ **8.** $2, -1, 3, -3, 2, 2, -1, -3, -1$

9. $25, -26, -25, 46, -55$ **10.** $-3, 0, 4, 5, -2, 8$

EXAMPLE 3 **Evaluating Expressions**

Evaluate the expression when $a = -15$, $b = 5$, and $c = -3$.

a. $\dfrac{a}{b}$ **b.** $\dfrac{bc}{a}$

Solution

a. $\dfrac{a}{b} = \dfrac{-15}{5}$ Substitute values.

     $= -3$ Different signs, so quotient is negative.

b. $\dfrac{bc}{a} = \dfrac{5 \cdot (-3)}{-15}$ Substitute values.

     $= \dfrac{-15}{-15}$ Multiply.

     $= 1$ Same sign, so quotient is positive.

Exercises for Example 3

Evaluate the expression when $a = -16$, $b = -2$, and $c = -8$.

11. $\dfrac{b}{a}$ **12.** $\dfrac{a}{bc}$ **13.** $\dfrac{c}{ab}$

Name _____ Date _____

Quick Catch-Up for Absent Students

For use with pages 77–81

The items checked below were covered in class on (date missed) _____

Lesson 2.5: Dividing Integers

____ **Goal:** Divide integers. (pp. 77–78)

Material Covered:

____ Example 1: Dividing Integers

____ Avoid errors

____ Guided Practice for Example 1

____ Example 2: Finding a Mean

____ Example 3: Evaluating Expressions

____ Guided Practice for Examples 2 and 3

Vocabulary:

mean, p. 78

____ Other (specify)

_____

Homework and Additional Learning Support

____ Textbook (specify) pp. 79–81

_____

____ *Study Guide* worksheet (specify exercises)

____ *@HomeTutor* for Lesson 2.5

____ Mixed Review of Problem Solving 2.1–2.5 (p. 82)

Problem Solving Workshop:
Mixed Problem Solving
For use with pages 57–81

1. **Multi-Step Problem** The table shows the earnings and expenses for a store for five months.

Month	Earnings	Expenses
March	$700	$900
April	$1300	$1100
May	$1100	$1400
June	$1900	$1500
July	$1700	$1300

a. For which months did the store earn more than it spent?

b. Write a positive or negative integer for the net profit or loss for each month.

c. How much money did the store make or lose during the five month period?

2. **Short Response** A steel ball is dropped from the top of a building that is 100 feet tall. The equation $h = -16t^2 + 100$ gives the ball's height h (in feet) above the ground after falling t seconds.

a. Find the ball's height when t is 2, 2.5, and 3 seconds.

b. Describe the position of the ball relative to the top of the building and to the ground for the values of t in part (a).

3. **Gridded Answer** What is the mean of the elevations relative to sea level, in meters?

40 m, −26 m, 0 m, −15 m, 32 m, 17 m

4. **Short Response** The table shows the high temperature in International Falls, Minnesota, for 5 days. Find the mean of the temperatures. Suppose the temperature on Friday was 5°F higher than what is shown in the table. How would this affect the mean? *Explain*.

Day	Temperature
Monday	−4°F
Tuesday	1°F
Wednesday	−2°F
Thursday	−5°F
Friday	−7°F

5. **Extended Response** The table shows the points scored and games played by 3 basketball players over their careers.

Player	Points	Games
Abdul-Jabbar	38,387	1560
Malone	36,928	1476
Jordan	32,292	1072

a. How many more points did Kareem Abdul-Jabbar score than Michael Jordan?

b. How many more games did Karl Malone play in than Michael Jordan?

c. Find the career points per game average for each player by dividing the points scored by games played. Round to the nearest tenth. Who had the highest career points per game average? *Explain*.

Name _____ Date _____

2.5 Real-World Problem Solving

For use with pages 77–81

Speed Limits

Some police officers have the task of making sure drivers observe the speed limit. Many drivers disregard the speed limit and drive too fast. Police officers issue citations to those who disobey the posted speed limit.

Use the following information in Exercises 1–3.

In Morton, Illinois, there is a small stretch of road where drivers often disregard the speed limit. Concerned residents approached the local police and asked them to do something to slow down the drivers. Officer Dunn was assigned to the problem. He decided on a four-week operation. The first week he would set up equipment to monitor and record the speed of passing vehicles. He wanted to document the average rate of speed of drivers prior to police intervention. This way he could prove that his measures had made a difference. The second week he would set up a sign that would flash the message, "Slow down! Your speed is:_____", where the blank shows the passing vehicle's speed. The third week, Officer Dunn would sit in his patrol car and use his radar gun to catch speed limit offenders. He would issue citations to those who disobeyed the speed limit. The fourth week he would once again put out the sign flashing a slow down message. Each week, Officer Dunn would record the average speeds and observe whether or not his plan made a difference. The table displays the data Officer Dunn recorded. The speed recorded is the average speed for that day.

Average Daily Driving Rates (mi/h)

	Mon	Tues	Wed	Thurs	Fri	Sat	Sun	Average for Week
Week 1	57	62	59	55	58	61	54	58 mi/h
Week 2	52	50	48	51	49	47	53	
Change	−5			−4				
Week 3	42	45	43	39	38	40	36	
Overall Change		−17				−21		
Week 4	36	38	39	34	35	37	35	
Overall Change			−20		−23			

1. Complete the table. Find each change by subtracting the day's average speed from the average speed during the corresponding day in week 1.

2. How much did the average speed for the week decrease by the end of the operation?

3. Officer Dunn's goal was to reduce the average speed to within 5 miles per hour of the speed limit. The speed limit on the road is 35 mi/h. Was the operation effective?

LESSON
2.5

Name _____ Date _____

Challenge Practice

For use with pages 77–81

A **geometric sequence** is a sequence of numbers for which each term in the sequence is found by multiplying the previous term by the same number. This number is called the **common ratio.** The common ratio is found by dividing any term by the previous term.

Example: Is 6, −12, 24, −48, 96, . . . a geometric sequence?

Solution: The common ratio is $\frac{-12}{6} = \frac{24}{-12} = \frac{-48}{24} = \frac{96}{-48} = -2$, so the sequence is geometric.

In Exercises 1–4, determine whether the sequence is geometric. If the sequence is geometric, find the common ratio.

1. 7, −7, 7, −7, . . .

2. −12, −9, −6, −3, . . .

3. −6, −6, −18, −36, . . .

4. 9, −3, 1, $-\frac{1}{3}$, $\frac{1}{9}$, . . .

In Exercises 5–8, write the first five terms of the geometric sequence with the given first term and given common ratio.

5. First term: −2
Common ratio: −3

6. First term: 10
Common ratio: −4

7. First term: −1000
Common ratio: 0.1

8. First term: $-\frac{1}{8}$
Common ratio: −2

9. Consider the geometric sequence with the first term 5 and the common ratio −2. What is the 7th term? the 10th term?

10. Use your results from Exercise 9 and the strategy *look for a pattern* to find a formula for the *n*th term of the geometric sequence.

LESSON
2.6

Teaching Guide

Lesson 2.6

Key Concept

You can use the commutative and associative properties of addition and multiplication to evaluate expressions using mental math. The commutative property enables you to add numbers of a sum in any order and multiply factors of a product in any order. The associative property allows you to change the grouping of number or factors without changing the sum or product, respectively.

Teaching the Lesson

Differentiating Instruction: See the Teacher's Edition side column notes on pages 85 and 86 and the notes on differentiating instruction in the *Course 3 Best Practices Toolkit*.

Teaching Notes and Suggested Questions: See the Teacher's Edition side column on page 84.

Activity Generator: See the Activity Generator Support Manual.

Starting the Lesson

Motivate the Lesson Use the information below to answer the questions at the right.

In February, Janet had withdrawals and deposits in her bank account of $20, −$35, −$16, −$42, −$115, $160, −$44, and $200.

Alternative Lesson Starter

You may want to review prerequisite concepts, such as:

- sum (p. 764)
- product (p. 768)

Questions to Start the Lesson

1. What was the total change in Janet's bank account for February?

2. In March, Janet had withdrawals and deposits in her bank account of −$50, −$35, −$72, $150, −$48, and $180. What was the total change in her bank account for March?

3. At the end of January, Janet had a total of $335 in her bank account. How much money was in her bank account at the end of March?

Common Student Errors

- Remind students that there are not commutative and associative properties of subtraction and division.

  Tip Review the root words of the property names. The root word of *commutative* is *commute*, meaning to *move*. The root word of *associative* is *associate*, meaning *joining together in a group*.

Example: Evaluate $25 − (15 − 7)$.

Student answer:

$25 − (15 − 7) = (25 − 15) − 7 = 10 − 7 = 3$

There is not an associative property of subtraction. To evaluate the expression, use the order of operations. The correct answer is 17.

Teaching Strategy of the Day

Student Preparation To prepare for a test, students should make a list of all of the lesson goals that will be covered on a test.

Teacher's Name _____ Class _____ Room _____ Date _____

Lesson Plan

Standard Schedule: 1 day lesson   Block Schedule: 0.5 day lesson with 2.5

GOAL   Use properties to evaluate expressions.

State Standards _____

Focus and Motivate

Starting Options
____ Homework Check (2.5): TE p. 79; Answer Transparencies
____ Daily Homework Quiz (2.5): TE p. 81
____ Warm-Up: Transparencies
____ Starting the Lesson Questions: Teaching Guide
____ Motivating the Lesson: TE p. 83

Teach

Teaching Options
____ Alternative Lesson Openers: Electronic Classroom
____ Classroom Activity: Activity Generator
____ Examples 1–4: PE pp. 83–85
____ Extra Examples 1–4: TE p. 84–85
____ Problem Solving: Using Alternative Methods: Chapter Resource Book p. 66
____ Notetaking Guide pp. 36–38

Checking for Understanding
____ Closing the Lesson: TE p. 85
____ Guided Practice Exercises: PE pp. 84–85

Practice and Apply

Assigning Homework
____ Basic: Day 1: pp. 85–87 Exs. 1–30, 38, 40–46, 50–54
____ Average: Day 1: pp. 85–87 Exs. 1–6, 8–14 even, 16–38, 40–47, 50–54
____ Advanced: Day 1: pp. 85–87 Exs. 1–6, 22, 29–39*, 44–49*, 53, 54
____ Block: pp. 85–87 Exs. 1–6, 8–14 even, 16–38, 40–47, 50–54 (with 2.5)
____ Practice Masters: Chapter Resource Book pp. 60–62 (Levels A, B, or C)

Assess and Reteach

Differentiating Instruction
____ Study Guide: Chapter Resource Book pp. 63–64
____ Tutorial Software
____ Challenge: Chapter Resource Book p. 67
____ Remediation and Intervention Package: _____
____ English Language Learners Package: _____

Preparing for Standardized Tests
____ Standardized Test Practice: PE pp. 86–87 Exs. 22, 44, 45, 54

Assessing the Lesson
____ Daily Homework Quiz (2.6): TE p. 87 or Transparencies

Name _____ Date _____

Practice A

For use with pages 83–87

Match the property to the equation that illustrates it.

1. Commutative Property of Addition

2. Commutative Property of Multiplication

3. Associative Property of Addition

4. Associative Property of Multiplication

A. $(ab)c = a(bc)$

B. $a + b = b + a$

C. $(a + b) + c = a + (b + c)$

D. $ab = ba$

Use a property of addition or multiplication to find the missing number. Name the property.

5. $(16 + 8) + \_\_\_\_ = 16 + (8 + 3)$

6. $5 \cdot 14 = 14 \cdot \_\_\_\_$

7. $(8 \cdot 12) \cdot \_\_\_\_ = 8 \cdot (12 \cdot 7)$

8. $11 + (3 + \_\_\_\_) = 11 + (5 + 3)$

Use the commutative property to evaluate.

9. $15 - (-13) + 25$

10. $-42 + 34 + (-8)$

11. $61 - 23 - 11$

12. $27 + (-41) + 93$

13. $7 \cdot (-121) \cdot 6$

14. $5 \cdot (-7) \cdot 20$

Use the associative property to evaluate.

15. $-22\left(\dfrac{1}{2} \cdot 15\right)$

16. $(-12 + 61) + 19$

17. $(3.7)(10 \times 7)$

In Exercises 18–20, simplify the expression.

18. $4 \cdot x \cdot (-8)$

19. $27 + (x - 19)$

20. $(74 + x) + 35$

21. A bank teller started the day with cash transactions of $40, −$33, $210, $50, and −$57. The positive numbers represent deposits and the negative numbers represent withdrawals. How did the amount of cash in the teller's drawer change?

22. Beth works 8 hours a day, 5 days a week as a cashier. She earns $7.25 an hour at her job. How much money does she make in a week?

Evaluate the expression.

23. $4.9 + 8.1 + (-5.9)$

24. $7 \cdot (5 \cdot 2 \cdot 3)$

25. $9(1.5)(6 \times 9)$

26. $\left(\dfrac{3}{4} + 3\right) - \dfrac{1}{4}$

27. $-\dfrac{2}{3} \cdot 19 \cdot 18$

28. $\left(\dfrac{5}{8} \cdot 13\right) \cdot 24$

29. The formula to determine the circumference of a circle is $C = 2\pi r$, where r is the radius of the circle, and π is approximately 3.14. If the radius of the circle is 50 cm, what is the circumference of the circle?

Name _____ Date _____

Practice B
For use with pages 83–87

Complete the equation to illustrate the property.

1. Commutative Property of Addition: $a + b =$ ____ + ____

2. Commutative Property of Multiplication: $ab =$ ____ • ____

3. Associative Property of Addition: $(a + b) + c =$ ____ + (____ + ____)

4. Associative Property of Multiplication: $(ab)c =$ ____ (____ • ____)

Use a property of addition or multiplication to find the missing number. Name the property.

5. $(21 + 17) +$ ____ $= 21 + (17 + 5)$

6. $12 \cdot 9 = 9 \cdot$ ____

7. $(16 \cdot 4) \cdot$ ____ $16 \cdot (4 \cdot 5)$

8. $26 + (37 +$ ____ $) = 26 + (51 + 37)$

Evaluate the expression.

9. $24 - (-19) + 26$

10. $-25 + 48 + (-75)$

11. $54 - 22 - 34$

12. $-11 + (-49 + 81)$

13. $(-15 + 43) + (-93)$

14. $500 \cdot 13 \cdot 12$

15. $\left(-13 \cdot \dfrac{2}{3}\right) \cdot 15$

16. $(-25) \cdot 9(-4)$

17. $1.1(8)(10)$

In Exercises 18–23, simplify the expression.

18. $6 \cdot x \cdot (-15)$

19. $-23 + [x + (-41)]$

20. $(57 + x) + 36$

21. $-15 + x - 49 + 17$

22. $37 + [x + (-52) + 18]$

23. $17 \cdot x \cdot 21$

24. A biscuit recipe calls for $\dfrac{3}{4}$ cup of milk, 2 cups of biscuit mix, $\dfrac{1}{4}$ cup of butter, and 1 cup of shredded cheddar cheese. How many cups of ingredients are there in all?

25. Ryan drives 17 miles north to do some errands. Then he drives another 26 miles north. His final errand is 7 miles south. How many miles north or south of his initial starting point does he end up?

Evaluate the expression.

26. $7.4 + 3.5 + (-5.4)$

27. $15 \cdot (8 \cdot 2 \cdot 3)$

28. $6(3 \times 9)(0.5)$

29. $\left(\dfrac{4}{5} + 2\right) - \dfrac{2}{5}$

30. $-\dfrac{1}{3} \cdot 13 \cdot 15$

31. $\left(\dfrac{3}{8} \cdot 11\right) \cdot 16$

Practice C

For use with pages 83–87

Lesson 2.6

Use a property of addition or multiplication to find the missing number. Name the property.

1. $(37 + 24) +$ ____ $= 37 + (24 + 15)$ **2.** $18 \cdot 41 = 41 \cdot$ ____

3. $(53 \cdot 14) \cdot$ ____ $= 53 \cdot (14 \cdot 22)$ **4.** $105 + (83 +$ ____$) = 105 + (42 + 83)$

Evaluate the expression.

5. $21 + (-37) + 19$

6. $-61 + (-46) + (-29)$

7. $5 \cdot (-36) \cdot 12$

8. $- + [51 + (-65)]$

9. $(-64 + 89) + (-36)$

10. $(20 \cdot 18) \cdot 5$

11. $-45\left(\frac{1}{5} \cdot 17\right)$

12. $(-32 \cdot 7) \cdot \frac{1}{2}$

13. $(4.6)(16)(10)$

In Exercises 14–19, simplify the expression.

14. $12 \cdot x(-8)$

15. $-45 + [x + (-73)]$

16. $(64 + x) + 25$

17. $-34 + x - 59 + 27$

18. $56 + [x + (-41) + 83]$

19. $15 \cdot x \cdot 29$

20. You are setting dinner tables for a party of 24 people. Each place setting gets 3 forks. You want to sit an even number of people at each of the four tables. How many forks will you need at each table?

21. Over the month, Stephanie made deposits of $107.50, $219.75, and $84.50 into her bank account. She also made withdrawals of $75.00 and $150.00. Her initial balance was $65.25. What was her final balance at the end of the month?

In Exercises 22–27, evaluate the expression.

22. $11.6 + 4 + (-11.6)$

23. $182 + 127 + 18$

24. $8(11 \times 5)(0.5)$

25. $\left(\frac{7}{9} + 6\right) - \frac{4}{9}$

26. $-\frac{1}{4} \cdot 21 \cdot 16$

27. $\left(\frac{5}{8} \cdot 17\right) \cdot 24$

28. Use the commutative properties of addition and multiplication to write three expressions equivalent to $3 + 9 \cdot 7$.

29. Terrell earns $8.50 per hour for mowing lawns. He worked 3.5 hours on Monday, 6.25 hours on Tuesday, 4.5 hours on Wednesday, 7 hours on Thursday, and 4.75 hours on Friday. How much money did Terrell earn for the week?

Name _____ Date _____

Study Guide
For use with pages 83–87

GOAL **Use properties to evaluate expressions.**

COMMUTATIVE PROPERTIES

Commutative Property of Addition

You can add the numbers of a sum in any order.

Algebra $a + b = b + a$

Commutative Property of Multiplication

You can multiply factors of a product in any order.

Algebra $ab = ba$

EXAMPLE 1 ## Using the Commutative Property

A furniture store sells a chair for $10. The furniture store sells 32 of the chairs a day. If the store is open 5 days a week, how much in weekly sales did the store generate by selling the chairs?

$$\boxed{\text{Weekly sales}} = \boxed{\begin{array}{c}\text{Number of chairs}\\\text{sold per day}\end{array}} \times \boxed{\begin{array}{c}\text{Cost per}\\\text{chair}\end{array}} \times \boxed{\begin{array}{c}\text{Number of days}\\\text{store is open}\end{array}}$$

$= 32 \cdot 10 \cdot 5$ Substitute values.

$= 32 \cdot 5 \cdot 10$ Commutative Property of Multiplication

$= 160 \cdot 10$ Multiply.

$= 1600$ Multiply.

The unit for the result is dollars per week. $\dfrac{\text{chairs}}{\text{day}} \times \dfrac{\text{dollars}}{\text{chair}} \times \dfrac{\text{days}}{\text{week}} = \dfrac{\text{dollars}}{\text{week}}$

Answer: The weekly sales generated by selling the chairs is $1600.

Exercises for Example 1

1. Determine the weekly sales if the furniture store sells 10 chairs a day at $12 a chair.

2. Determine the weekly sales if the furniture store sells 16 chairs a day at $10 a chair.

Lesson 2.6

Study Guide
For use with pages 83–87

EXAMPLE 2 ## Using the Commutative Property

$$-46 + 25 - 14 = -46 + 25 + (-14) \qquad \text{Change subtraction to addition.}$$
$$= -46 + (-14) + 25 \qquad \text{Commutative Property of Addition}$$
$$= -60 + 25 \qquad \text{Add } -46 \text{ and } -14.$$
$$= -35 \qquad \text{Add.}$$

Exercises for Example 2

Use the commutative property to evaluate.

3. $4 \cdot (-6) \cdot 5$ **4.** $26 + (-78) - (-34)$ **5.** $89 - 51 - 29$

EXAMPLE 3 ## Using the Associative Property

$$\frac{-2}{7} + \left(\frac{-5}{7} + 6\right) = \left(\frac{-2}{7} + \frac{-5}{7}\right) + 6 \qquad \text{Associative Property of Addition}$$

$$= \frac{-7}{7} + 6 \qquad \text{Add fractions.}$$

$$= -1 + 6 \qquad \text{Write } \frac{-7}{7} \text{ as } -1.$$

$$= 5 \qquad \text{Add.}$$

EXAMPLE 4 ## Using the Associative Property

$$-2(11 \cdot 50) = -2(50 \cdot 11) \qquad \text{Commutative Property of Multiplication}$$
$$= (-2 \cdot 50) \cdot 11 \qquad \text{Associative Property of Multiplication}$$
$$= (-100) \cdot 11 \qquad \text{Multiply.}$$
$$= -1100 \qquad \text{Multiply.}$$

Exercises for Examples 3 and 4

Use the associative property to evaluate.

6. $66(-20)(5)$ **7.** $140 - 60 + 17$ **8.** $-5 + 36 - 95$
9. $5 \cdot 17 \cdot 2$ **10.** $43(-2)(50)$ **11.** $10 \cdot (-7) \cdot 10$
12. $-8 + 35 + 15$ **13.** $12 + 17 + (-2) + 3$ **14.** $24 \cdot 13 \cdot 0$

Name _____ Date _____

Quick Catch-Up for Absent Students

For use with pages 83–87

The items checked below were covered in class on (date missed) _____

Lesson 2.6: Number Properties

_____ **Goal:** Use properties to evaluate expressions. (pp. 83–85)

Material Covered:

_____ Example 1: Using the Commutative Property

_____ Example 2: Using the Commutative Property

_____ Simplify computations

_____ Guided Practice for Examples 1 and 2

_____ Example 3: Using the Associative Property

_____ Review adding fractions

_____ Example 4: Using the Associative Property

_____ Vocabulary

_____ Guided Practice for Examples 3 and 4

_____ Other (specify)

_____

Homework and Additional Learning Support

_____ Textbook (specify) pp. 85–87

_____

_____ *Study Guide* worksheet (specify exercises)

_____ *@HomeTutor* for Lesson 2.6

Name _____ Date _____

Problem Solving Workshop:
Using Alternative Methods

For use with pages 83–87

Another Way to Solve Example 1 on page 83

Multiple Representations In Example 1 on page 83, you saw how to solve a problem about a bike trip using the commutative property. You can also solve the problem by *making a table.*

PROBLEM **Tour Biking** You are going on a 400 mile bike trip. You plan to cycle at an average speed of 12 miles per hour for 7 hours a day. Can you complete the trip in 5 days?

METHOD **Making a Table** You can solve the problem by making a table.

STEP 1 Find the distance you can cycle in one day. Use the distance formula.

$d = r \cdot t$ Write distance formula.

$= 12 \cdot 7$ Substitute 12 for r and 7 for t.

$= 84$ Multiply.

You can cycle a distance of 84 miles in one day.

STEP 2 Make a table showing the total distance cycled for 5 days.

Day	1	2	3	4	5
Distance (miles)	84	168	252	336	420

After 5 days, you can cycle a distance of 420 miles. Because 400 miles is less than the 420 miles you can travel in 5 days, you can complete the trip in 5 days.

PRACTICE

1. **What If?** Suppose in the Example you plan to cycle at an average speed of 10 miles per hour for 6 hours a day. Can you complete the trip in 6 days?

2. **Football** During a football game, seven players rushed the football for 68 yards, 39 yards, 32 yards, 11 yards, 6 yards, 4 yards, and −7 yards. What was the total number of rushing yards?

3. **Work** Jodi plans to work 5 hours a day for 3 days this week. Her hourly wage is $7 per hour. How much money does she plan to earn this week?

4. **Sweaters** You buy 4 sweaters that cost $27 each. The store is offering a discount of $\frac{1}{2}$ off the original price. What is the total cost of the sweaters after the discount?

Name _____ Date _____

Challenge Practice

For use with pages 83–87

1. Is division associative? Justify your answer with an example.

2. Is subtraction commutative? Justify your answer with an example.

3. Is subtraction associative? Justify your answer with an example.

4. You put on your sock and then put on your shoe. Are these actions commutative? Explain your reasoning.

5. While in your car, you turn on the radio and then turn on the air conditioning. Are these actions commutative? Explain your reasoning.

6. Give an example of two activities that are commutative.

7. Give an example of two activities that are not commutative.

McDougal Littell Math, Course 3   **67**
Chapter 2   Resource Book

Teacher's Name _____ Class _____ Room _____ Date _____

Teaching Guide

Key Concept

The distributive property is used to simplify and evaluate expressions that involve the product of a number and a sum or difference. Applying the distributive property to an expression produces an equivalent expression, which can often be simplified by combining like terms.

Teaching the Lesson

Differentiating Instruction: See the Teacher's Edition side column notes on pages 90 and 91 and the notes on differentiating instruction in the *Course 3 Best Practices Toolkit*.

Teaching Notes and Suggested Questions: See the Teacher's Edition side columns on pages 89–90.

Activity Generator: See the Activity Generator Support Manual.

Animated Math: You may want to include the animation on page 91 in your lesson.

Starting the Lesson

Motivate the Lesson Use the information below to answer the questions at the right.

You and two friends go to a bowling alley. You decide to pay for everyone's bowling and lunch. You each play one game of bowling that costs $3. You each have a juice that costs $1 and slice of pizza that costs $1.25. How much do you pay at the bowling alley?

Alternative Lesson Starter

You could also use a trip to a roller skating rink. You could use a problem involving the difference of the areas of two rectangular gardens.

Questions to Start the Lesson

1. Find the total number of games of bowling played by you and your two friends.

2. How many juices do you buy? How many slices of pizza do you buy?

3. Write an expression for the amount you pay at the bowling alley.

4. Use the distributive property to evaluate the expression. How much do you pay at the bowling alley?

Common Student Errors

• Students may have difficulty with the signs when distributing a negative number.

  Tip As with Lesson 2.6, you may wish to review the root word of the property name. The root word of *distributive* is *distribute*, meaning *to give out* or *to dole out*.

Example: Use the distributive property to evaluate $-6(-5 + 9)$.

Student answer: $-6(-5 + 9) = -30 - 54$
$$= -84$$

The product $-6(-5)$ is 30. The correct answer is -24.

Teaching Strategy of the Day

Motivating Students Set up a tally chart on the blackboard so that as students walk into the classroom they can mark the homework problems they would like to see solved. Student volunteers can then solve the most requested problems on the blackboard.

Teacher's Name _____ Class _____ Room _____ Date_____

Lesson Plan

Standard Schedule: 1 day lesson   Block Schedule: 0.5 day lesson with 2.8

GOAL   Use the distributive property.

State Standards _____

Focus and Motivate   **Starting Options**
____ Homework Check (2.6): TE p. 86; Answer Transparencies
____ Daily Homework Quiz (2.6): TE p. 87
____ Warm-Up: Transparencies
____ Starting the Lesson Questions: Teaching Guide
____ Motivating the Lesson: TE p. 88

Teach   **Teaching Options**
____ Alternative Lesson Openers: Electronic Classroom
____ Classroom Activity: Activity Generator
____ Examples 1–4: PE pp. 88–90
____ Extra Examples 1–4: TE p. 89–90
____ Notetaking Guide pp. 39s–41

Checking for Understanding
____ Closing the Lesson: TE p. 90
____ Guided Practice Exercises: PE pp. 89–90

Practice and Apply   **Assigning Homework**
____ Basic: Day 1: pp. 90–92 Exs. 1–32, 37, 44–48, 52–58
____ Average: Day 1: pp. 90–92 Exs. 1–4, 6–32 even, 37, 42, 44–48, 52–58
____ Advanced: Day 1: pp. 90–92 Exs. 1–4, 15, 28–43*, 46–51*, 58
____ Block: pp. 90–92 Exs. 1–4, 6–32 even, 37, 42, 44–48, 52–58 (with 2.8)
____ Practice Masters: Chapter Resource Book pp. 70–72 (Levels A, B, or C)

Assess and Reteach   **Differentiating Instruction**
____ Study Guide: Chapter Resource Book pp. 73–74
____ Tutorial Software
____ Challenge: Chapter Resource Book p. 76
____ Remediation and Intervention Package: _____
____ English Language Learners Package: _____

Preparing for Standardized Tests
____ Standardized Test Practice: PE pp. 90–92 Exs. 15, 37, 45, 46, 48, 49, 58

Assessing the Lesson
____ Daily Homework Quiz (2.7): TE p. 92 or Transparencies

Lesson 2.7

LESSON 2.7

Practice A

For use with pages 88–93

Match the expression with its simplified expression.

1. $6(x + 7)$ **2.** $7(x + 6)$ **3.** $3(2x - 14)$ **4.** $x(5 + 7)$

A. $6x - 42$ **B.** $6x + 42$ **C.** $7x + 42$ **D.** $12x$

Use the distributive property to write an equivalent expression.

5. $-6(4 + 3)$ **6.** $8(9 + 4)$ **7.** $2(6 + 7)$

8. $-4(x + 3)$ **9.** $5(2 + x)$ **10.** $6(x - 3)$

Simplify the expression by combining like terms.

11. $m + 4m$ **12.** $8x + 7y + 2x$ **13.** $15m + 11p - p$

14. $9c + 11d - 3c - 4d$ **15.** $-5x - 7y + 2x - 9y$ **16.** $3x + 4y + 7x - 8y - 5$

In Exercises 17–19, use the following information. You work for 8 hours. You earn $7.50 an hour. The amount you earn is 8(7.50).

17. Write $8(7.50)$ as 8 times the sum of a whole number and a decimal.

18. Find the products of 8 and the whole number and of 8 and the decimal.

19. Find the sum of the products.

Find the total area of the two rectangles.

20.

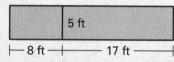

21.

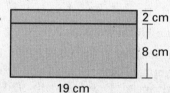

In Exercises 22–27, simplify the expression.

22. $9(w - 6)$ **23.** $7x(4 + 3 - 5)$ **24.** $7x - 3 + 9x - 4x$

25. $8(d + 4d) - 3d$ **26.** $9p - (7p + p)$ **27.** $9(3g - 5) + 6 - 4g$

28. You are buying lunch at a cafeteria for yourself and three friends. Each of you orders a turkey sandwich that costs $3.75 and a glass of lemonade that costs $1.25. There is no tax or tip. Explain how to use mental math to find the total cost of the food and drinks.

29. Your front yard is 50 feet wide and 60 feet deep. Your back yard is 50 feet wide and 140 feet deep. What is the combined area of your front and back yards?

Lesson 2.7

Name _____ Date _____

Practice B

For use with pages 88–93

Use the distributive property to write an equivalent expression.

1. $-5(y + 7)$

2. $4(11 + 6)$

3. $6(8 + m)$

4. $-31(24 + 12)$

5. $13[7 + w + (-9)]$

6. $-29(p - 21 - 5)$

Simplify the expression by combining like terms.

7. $c + 8c + 5d$

8. $4m + 3k + 6m + 9k$

9. $8s + 6t - (-5s) - 2t$

10. $15c + 12d - 7d - 3c$

11. $-16g + 3h - 19h - 4g$

12. $8x + 5y + 11x - 2y$

Find the total area of the two rectangles.

13.

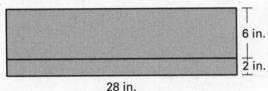

28 in.

6 in.

2 in.

14.

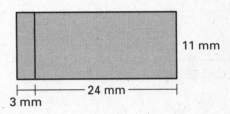

11 mm

24 mm

3 mm

In Exercises 15–20, simplify the expression.

15. $12(w - 8)$

16. $-3x(7 + 8 - 4)$

17. $11x - 8 + 5x - 9x$

18. $7(d + 5d) - 16d$

19. $13p - (8p + 7p) + 12p$

20. $11(2g - 4) + 12 - 18g$

21. A bride is buying gifts for the seven attendants in her bridal party. She wants to get each a necklace for \$21.85 and a pair of earrings for \$8.15. Explain how to use mental math to find how much money she will need for these gifts.

22. Delia wants to put tint on windows that have the dimensions shown at the right. The material for the tint costs \$1.99 per square foot. How much will it cost to buy enough material for both windows?

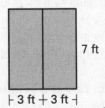

7 ft

3 ft 3 ft

In Exercises 23–26, find the product using mental math and the distributive property.

23. $7(15)$

24. $4(23)$

25. $12(18)$

26. $30(52)$

27. A company is putting vinyl siding up across the back of two condominium units. Both units are 15 feet high. One unit is 27 feet wide and the other is 31 feet wide. Write an expression for the area of siding needed. Then find the amount.

Name_____ Date _____

Practice C

For use with pages 88–93

Use the distributive property to write an equivalent expression.

1. $-9(y + 6)$ **2.** $7(15 - 8)$ **3.** $5(7 + m + 13)$

4. $-12[4 + w + (-6)]$ **5.** $-24(p - 22 - 15)$ **6.** $35(21 + 17 + 3x)$

Simplify the expression by combining like terms.

7. $3c + 9c + 7d$ **8.** $7m + 6k + 15m + 18k$ **9.** $13s + 6t - (-9s) - 4t$

10. $18c - 23c + 17d - 13d$ **11.** $-23g + 18h - 14h - 7g$ **12.** $11x + 4 + 3y - 7$

Find the total area of the two rectangles.

13.

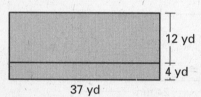

12 yd
4 yd
37 yd

14.

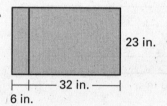

23 in.
32 in.
6 in.

In Exercises 15–20, simplify the expression.

15. $15(w - 12)$ **16.** $-6x(19 + 13 - 14)$ **17.** $13x - 7 + 5x - 17x$

18. $19(d + 4d) - 26d$ **19.** $27p - (9p + 12p) + 23p$ **20.** $-12(3g - 6)$

21. You order 3 pizzas, all with one extra item. The cost of each pizza is
$6.45 plus $.55 for the extra item. You also have a coupon to get $1 off
each pizza. Use mental math to find the total cost of the three pizzas.

22. Your parents are putting new flooring in the kitchen, which is 12 feet wide
and 17 feet long. They are putting vinyl tile on an area that is 7 feet by
12 feet, and they are carpeting the rest of the floor. The carpet costs
$1.50 per square foot. How much will the carpeting cost?

**In Exercises 23–26, find the product using mental math and the
distributive property.**

23. $8(19)$ **24.** $6(27)$ **25.** $12(13)$ **26.** $16(24)$

27. Your school drama club is ordering tickets to a play. Each ticket costs
$20.25. There is a $3.50 handling fee per ticket. There is also a $5 shipping
fee for sending all of the tickets to your school. Write an expression to
find your total cost for x tickets. What would the cost be for 25 tickets?
What would the cost be for 50 tickets?

Name _____ Date _____

Study Guide

For use with pages 88–93

GOAL Use the distributive property.

VOCABULARY

In a sum, the parts that are added together are the **terms** of an expression. You can use the distributive property to combine *like terms*. **Like terms** have identical variable parts raised to the same power. In a term, the number multiplied by the variable is the **coefficient** of the variable.

DISTRIBUTIVE PROPERTY

$a(b + c) = ab + ac$ $\qquad\qquad$ $a(b - c) = ab - ac$

EXAMPLE 1 **Finding a Combined Area**

Find the total area of the two rectangles.

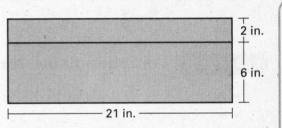

Method 1 Find the area of each rectangle, then find the total area.

Area = 2(21) + 6(21)

= 42 + 126

= 168 square inches

Method 2 Find the total width and then multiply by the common length.

Area = 21(2 + 6)

= 21(8)

= 168 square inches

Answer: The total area of the two rectangles is 168 square inches.

Exercises for Example 1

Find the total area.

1.

2.

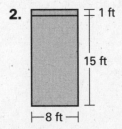

Lesson 2.7

Name _____ Date _____

Study Guide
For use with pages 88-93

EXAMPLE 2 **Using the Distributive Property**

a. $-3(x - 5) = -3(x) - (-3)(5)$ Distributive Property

            $= -3x - (-15)$ Multiply.

            $= -3x + 15$ To subtract -15, add 15.

b. $4(1 - 12 - 5) = 4(1) - 4(12) - 4(5)$ Distributive Property

                $= 4 - 48 - 20$ Multiply.

                $= 4 + (-48) + (-20)$ To subtract 48 and 20,

                                          add -48 and -20.

                $= -64$ Add.

Exercises for Example 2

Use the distributive property to evaluate the expression.

3. $-3(4 + 11)$ **4.** $-6(-16 - 12)$ **5.** $5(8 - 13)$

6. $2(w - 9)$ **7.** $-8(7 - y)$ **8.** $-z(1 - 2)$

EXAMPLE 3 **Combining Like Terms**

a. $7x + 5x = (7 + 5)x$ $7x$ and $5x$ are like terms.

        $= 12x$ Add.

b. $-6y + 8y + 9 = (-6 + 8)y + 9$ Add coefficients of like terms.

             $= 2y + 9$ Add.

EXAMPLE 4 **Simplifying Expressions**

$3(7 - x) + 4x = 21 - 3x + 4x$ Distributive Property

            $= 21 + (-3x) + 4x$ Change subtraction to addition.

            $= 21 + (-3 + 4)x$ Distributive Property

            $= 21 + x$ Simplify.

Exercises for Examples 3 and 4

Simplify the expression by combining like terms.

9. $r + 3r - 8r$ **10.** $16w - 5w - 7w + 12w$

11. $-2x + 5x + 3y - 9y$ **12.** $r + 10r - (-4r) - r$

Name _____ Date _____

Quick Catch-Up for Absent Students

For use with pages 88–93

The items checked below were covered in class on (date missed) _____

Lesson 2.7: The Distributive Property

____ **Goal:** Use the distributive property. (pp. 88–90)

Material Covered:

____ Example 1: Finding a Combined Area

____ Example 2: Using the Distributive Property

____ Guided Practice for Examples 1 and 2

____ Take notes

____ Example 3: Combining Like Terms

____ Example 4: Simplifying an Expression

____ Avoid errors

____ Guided Practice for Examples 3 and 4

Vocabulary:

distributive property, p. 88   terms, p. 89

like terms, p. 89   coefficient, p. 89

constant term, p. 89

Technology Activity 2.7: Using Integer Operations

____ **Goal:** Use a calculator to evaluate expressions. (p. 93)

____ Other (specify)

_____

Homework and Additional Learning Support

____ Textbook (specify) pp. 90–92

_____

____ *Study Guide* worksheet (specify exercises)

____ @*HomeTutor* for Lesson 2.7

McDougal Littell Math, Course 3 **75**

Lesson 2.7

LESSON 2.7

Challenge Practice

For use with pages 88–93

In Lesson 2.7, you learned that the distributive property can be applied to multiplication over an expression involving a sum or difference of two or more numbers.

1. Does $\dfrac{36 - 4}{4} = \dfrac{36}{4} - \dfrac{4}{4}$?

2. Use the result from Exercise 1 to determine whether the distributive property can be applied to *division* over an expression involving a difference.

3. Does $\dfrac{40 + 15}{5} = \dfrac{40}{5} + \dfrac{15}{5}$?

4. Use the result from Exercise 3 to determine whether the distributive property can be applied to *division* over an expression involving a sum.

5. Does $(2 + 4)^2 = 2^2 + 4^2$?

6. Use the result from Exercise 5 to determine whether the distributive property can be applied to *powers* over an expression involving a sum.

7. Does $(2 \cdot 4)^2 = 2^2 \cdot 4^2$?

8. Use the result from Exercise 7 to determine whether the distributive property can be applied to *powers* over an expression involving a product.

McDougal Littell Math, Course 3
Chapter 2   Resource Book

Lesson 2.7

LESSON 2.8
Teaching Guide

Key Concept

You can identify and plot points in a coordinate plane. Points are represented by ordered pairs, where the first number is the x-coordinate and the second number is the y-coordinate.

Teaching the Lesson

Differentiating Instruction: See the Teacher's Edition side column notes on page 96 and the notes on differentiating instruction in the *Course 3 Best Practices Toolkit*.

Teaching Notes and Suggested Questions: See the Teacher's Edition side column on page 95.

Activity Generator: See the Activity Generator Support Manual.

Animated Math: You may want to include the animation on page 97 in your lesson.

Starting the Lesson

Motivate the Lesson You can use a coordinate plane to find the perimeter and area of a garden. Use the information below to answer the questions at the right.

The points A(−3, 4), B(4, 4), C(4, −1), and D(−3, −1) form a rectangular garden.

Alternative Lesson Starter

You can also find the perimeter and area of a rectangular deck.

Questions to Start the Lesson

1. Plot the points in a coordinate plane.

2. Find the perimeter of the rectangle that represents the garden.

3. Find the area of the rectangle that represents the garden.

4. The length and width of each small square on the coordinate plane represents 2 feet. Find the perimeter of the garden in feet. Find the area of the garden in square feet.

Common Student Errors

- Students often label the quadrants incorrectly.

  Tip Be sure that students label the upper right–hand quadrant as Quadrant I and continue to label the quadrants in order in a counterclockwise direction. Tell students that in Quadrant I both the x-coordinate and the y-coordinate of points are *positive*, making this a "*positive*" place to start.

Example: What quadrant is the point (−5, 3) located in?

Student answer: Quadrant I

Quadrant I is the upper right-hand quadrant in the coordinate plane. The correct answer is Quadrant II.

Teaching Strategy of the Day

Testing Insist that students show all of their work when solving a problem on a test. Give partial credit to the student who makes a mathematical error, but demonstrates an understanding of the lesson goals.

Teacher's Name _____ Class _____ Room _____ Date_____

Lesson Plan

Standard Schedule: 1 day lesson   Block Schedule: 0.5 day lesson with 2.7

GOAL   **Identify and plot points in a coordinate plane.**

State Standards _____

Focus and Motivate	**Starting Options**
	____ Homework Check (2.7): TE p. 91; Answer Transparencies
	____ Daily Homework Quiz (2.7): TE p. 92
	____ Warm-Up: Transparencies
	____ Starting the Lesson Questions: Teaching Guide
	____ Motivating the Lesson: TE p. 94

Teach   **Teaching Options**

____ Alternative Lesson Openers: Electronic Classroom

____ Classroom Activity: Activity Generator

____ Examples 1–3: PE pp. 94–95

____ Extra Examples 1–3: TE p. 95

____ Problem Solving: Mixed Problem Solving: Chapter Resource Book p. 86

____ Notetaking Guide pp. 42–44

Checking for Understanding

____ Closing the Lesson: TE p. 95

____ Guided Practice Exercises: PE pp. 94–95

Practice and Apply   **Assigning Homework**

____ Basic: Day 1: pp. 96–100 Exs. 1–28, 36–42, 46, 51–60

____ Average: Day 1: pp. 96–100 Exs. 1, 2, 4–32 even, 36–45, 51–60

____ Advanced: Day 1: pp. 96–100 Exs. 1, 2, 23, 28–36*, 42–50*, 57–60

____ Block: pp. 96–100 Exs. 1, 2, 4–32 even, 36–45, 51–60 (with 2.7)

____ Practice Masters: Chapter Resource Book pp. 80–82 (Levels A, B, or C)

Assess and Reteach   **Differentiating Instruction**

____ Study Guide: Chapter Resource Book pp. 83–84

____ Tutorial Software

____ Challenge: Chapter Resource Book p. 87

____ Remediation and Intervention Package: _____

____ English Language Learners Package: _____

Preparing for Standardized Tests

____ Standardized Test Practice: PE pp. 96–99 Exs. 28, 36, 38, 41, 42, 46, 60

____ Building Test–Taking Skills: PE pp. 108–111

Assessing the Lesson

____ Daily Homework Quiz (2.8): TE p. 99 or Transparencies

LESSON 2.8 Technology Activity

For use with pages 94–100

GOAL Use a graphing calculator to plot points in a coordinate plane.

EXAMPLE

You can plot points in a coordinate plane using a graphing calculator's *point on feature*. Use a graphing calculator to plot the following.

a. $(-3, 7)$ **b.** $(4, -2)$ **c.** $(-6, -8)$

Solution

Before plotting the points, press ZOOM 6 to set the viewing window to the standard view. If necessary, press DRAW ENTER to clear the viewing window of other graphs. Then press 2nd [QUIT] to return to the home screen.

Keystrokes   **Display**

a.

b.

c. DRAW ENTER 2nd [QUIT] DRAW
▶ ENTER (-) 6 , (-) 8) ENTER

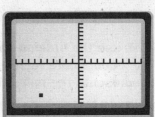

your turn now Use a graphing calculator to plot the point.
Then describe the point's location. In which quadrant does the point lie?

1. $(-4, 5)$ **2.** $(-8, -3)$

3. $(9, 6)$ **4.** $(-5, 9)$

5. $(2, -3)$ **6.** $(4, 3)$

7. $(-7, -8)$ **8.** $(6, -2)$

Lesson 2.8

Name _____ Date _____

Practice A

For use with pages 94–100

Identify the label showing the given part of the graph.

1. *x*-axis
2. *y*-axis
3. Quadrant I
4. Quadrant II
5. Quadrant III
6. Quadrant IV
7. Origin
8. *x*-coordinate
9. *y*-coordinate

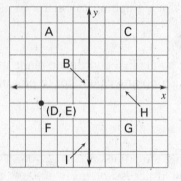

Give the coordinates of the point.

10. *A*
11. *B*
12. *C*
13. *D*
14. *E*
15. *F*

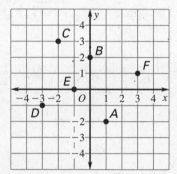

Plot the point in a coordinate plane and describe its location.

16. $(3, -2)$
17. $(0, 4)$
18. $(7, 6)$
19. $(1, -5)$
20. $(-3, 7)$
21. $(-4, -8)$

Plot and connect the given points. Then identify the resulting figure and find its perimeter.

22. $(2, 0), (2, -3), (4, -3), (4, 0)$
23. $(7, 2), (7, 6), (2, 6), (2, 2)$
24. $(1, 5), (-3, 5), (-3, 1), (1, 1)$

In Exercises 25–26, use the ordered pairs below that give data, for a road trip. The *x*-coordinate represents the hours driven, and the *y*-coordinate represents the miles traveled.

(1, 60), (2, 120), (3, 180), (4, 240), (5, 300)

25. Plot the points in the coordinate plane. Identify the pattern.

26. Use the pattern to estimate the miles traveled if you have driven for $3\frac{1}{2}$ hours.

27. Plot and connect the points. Find the perimeter and the area of the rectangle formed.

   $A(3, 7), B(3, 1), C(-5, 1), D(-5, 7)$

Name _____ Date _____

Practice B

For use with pages 94–100

Give the coordinates of the point.

1. A 2. D

3. B 4. E

5. C 6. F

Plot the point in a coordinate plane and describe its location.

7. $(-5, 3)$ 8. $(1, -4)$

9. $(0, -1)$ 10. $(3, 7)$

11. $(-6, 0)$ 12. $(-8, -5)$

Plot and connect the given points. Then identify the resulting figure and find its perimeter.

13. $(-1, 0), (-1, 4), (-4, 4), (-4, 0)$

14. $(3, -5), (3, 3), (-2, 3), (-2, -5)$

15. $(-6, -3), (-6, 2), (-1, 2), (-1, -3)$

In Exercises 16–17, use the ordered pairs below that give data for the amount of money you earn at a new job. The *x*-coordinate represents the number of hours you work and the *y*-coordinate represents the amount of money you earn.

(1, $8.50), (2, $17.00), (3, $25.50), (4, $34.00)

16. Plot the points in a coordinate plane. Identify the pattern.

17. Use the pattern to estimate the amount of money you would earn if you work 6 hours.

In Exercises 18–20, plot and connect the points. Find the perimeter and the area of the rectangle formed.

18. $A(7, -2), B(7, 3), C(-1, 3), D(-1, -2)$

19. $W(-5, 6), X(2, 6), Y(2, 0), Z(-5, 0)$

20. $J(0, 0), K(0, -5), L(-6, -5), M(-6, 0)$

Name _____ Date _____

Practice C
For use with pages 94–100

Give the coordinates of the point.

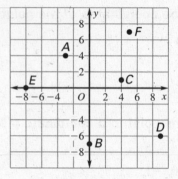

1. A

2. D

3. B

4. E

5. C

6. F

Plot the point in a coordinate plane and describe its location.

7. $(6, -2)$

8. $(-4, 1)$

9. $(0, -5)$

10. $(9, 3)$

11. $(-2, -7)$

12. $(-1, 0)$

Plot and connect the given points. Then identify the resulting figure and find its perimeter.

13. $(2, 2), (2, 6), (-2, 6), (-2, 2)$

14. $(-4, -9), (1, -9), (1, 1), (-4, 1)$

15. $(5, -3), (5, 8), (-3, 8), (-3, -3)$

In Exercises 16–18, suppose that you can run distances at a rate of 7 minutes per mile.

16. Find the number of minutes it takes you to run 1 mile, 2 miles, 3 miles, and 4 miles.

17. Plot the times that you found in Exercise 16 in a coordinate plane, where the x-coordinate represents the number of miles and the y-coordinate represents the number of minutes.

18. Draw a line through the points. Use the line to estimate the number of minutes it would take you to run 7 miles.

In Exercises 19–21, plot and connect the points. Find the perimeter and area of the rectangle formed.

19. $A(4, -7), B(4, 7), C(-1, 7), D(-1, -7)$

20. $W(-3, 2), X(2, 2), Y(2, -1), Z(-3, -1)$

21. $J(0, 4), K(-8, 4), L(-8, -2), M(0, -2)$

22. Draw a rectangle that has coordinates only in the first quadrant. Multiply each coordinate by 3 and draw this rectangle. Compare this rectangle with the original one and compare their perimeters. What do you find?

LESSON 2.8

Study Guide

For use with pages 94–100

GOAL Identify and plot points in a coordinate plane.

VOCABULARY

A **coordinate plane** is formed by the intersection of a horizontal number line called the **x-axis** and a vertical number line called the **y-axis**. The axes meet at a point called the **origin** and divide the coordinate plane into four **quadrants**.

Points in a coordinate plane are represented by **ordered pairs**. The first number is the **x-coordinate**. The second number is the **y-coordinate**.

EXAMPLE 1 **Naming Points in the Coordinate Plane**

Give the coordinates of the point.

a. *A*

b. *B*

c. *C*

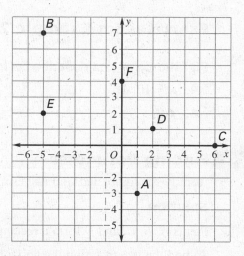

Solution

a. Point *A* is 1 unit to the right of the origin and 3 units down. So, the x-coordinate is 1 and the y-coordinate is -3. The point is $A(1, -3)$.

b. Point *B* is 5 units to the left of the origin and 7 units up. So, the x-coordinate is -5 and the y-coordinate is 7. The point is $B(-5, 7)$.

c. Point *C* is 6 units to the right of the origin. So, the x-coordinate is 6 and the y-coordinate is 0. The point is $C(6, 0)$.

Exercises for Example 1

Give the coordinates of the point.

1. *D*   **2.** *E*   **3.** *F*

Lesson 2.8

Name _____ Date _____

Study Guide

For use with pages 94–100

EXAMPLE 2 **Graphing Points in the Coordinate Plane**

Plot the point and describe its location.

a. $A(-3, 6)$

b. $B(9, -8)$

c. $C(-4, 0)$

Solution

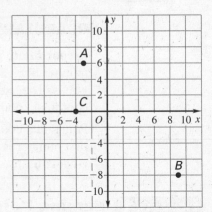

a. Begin at the origin, move 3 units to the left, then 6 units up. Point A lies in Quadrant II.

b. Begin at the origin, move 9 units to the right, then 8 units down. Point B lies in Quadrant IV.

c. Begin at the origin, move 4 units to the left. Point C lies on the x-axis.

Exercises for Example 2

Plot the point and describe its location.

4. $R(-10, 4)$ **5.** $S(5, -8)$

6. $T(0, -6)$ **7.** $U(1, -1)$

EXAMPLE 3 **Finding Perimeter**

Identify the figure and find its perimeter.

Solution

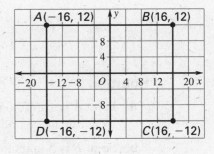

Points A, B, C, and D form a rectangle.

To find the length ℓ, find the horizontal distance from A to B.

$\ell = |x\text{-coordinate of } A - x\text{-coordinate of } B|$
$= |-16 - 16| = |-32| = 32$

To find the width w, find the vertical distance from A to D.
$w = |y\text{-coordinate of } A - y\text{-coordinate of } D| = |12 - (-12)| = |24| = 24$

Perimeter $= 2\ell + 2w = 2(32) + 2(24) = 112$

Answer: The rectangle has a perimeter of 112 units.

Exercise for Example 3

Plot and connect the given points. Then identify the resulting figure and find its perimeter.

8. $A(-5, 3)$, $B(3, 3)$, $C(3, -5)$, $D(-5, -5)$

Lesson 2.8

LESSON
2.8

Name _____ Date _____

Quick Catch-Up for Absent Students

For use with pages 94–100

The items checked below were covered in class on (date missed) _____

Lesson 2.8: The Coordinate Plane

_____ **Goal:** Identify and plot points in a coordinate plane. (pp. 94–95)

Material Covered:

_____ Example 1: Naming Points in a Coordinate Plane

_____ Guided Practice for Example 1

_____ Example 2: Graphing Points in a Coordinate Plane

_____ Vocabulary

_____ Example 3: Solve a Multi-Step Problem

_____ Finding distances

_____ Guided Practice for Examples 2 and 3

Vocabulary:

coordinate plane, p. 94 x-axis, y-axis, p. 94

origin, p. 94   quadrant, p. 94

ordered pair, p. 94 x- and y-coordinates, p. 94

_____ Other (specify)

_____

Homework and Additional Learning Support

_____ Textbook (specify) pp. 96–100

_____

_____ *Study Guide* worksheet (specify exercises)

_____ *@HomeTutor* for Lesson 2.8

_____ Mixed Review of Problem Solving 2.6–2.8 (p. 101)

Lesson 2.8

Name _____ Date _____

Problem Solving Workshop:
Mixed Problem Solving

For use with pages 83–99

Lesson 2.8

1. **Multi-Step Problem** Use the coordinate plane shown.

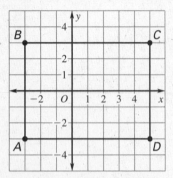

   a. Write and evaluate a numerical expression for the length and width of the rectangle.

   b. Find the perimeter and area of the rectangle.

   c. Each unit in the coordinate plane represents 10 feet. Use this information to find the perimeter and area of the rectangle.

2. **Multi-Step Problem** A gas station charges $2.50 per gallon of gasoline.

   a. Find the costs of buying 3 gallons, 4 gallons, and 5 gallons of gasoline.

   b. Plot the costs you found in part (a) in a coordinate plane, where the x-coordinate represents the number of gallons of gasoline and the y-coordinate represents the cost, in dollars, of the gasoline.

   c. Draw a line through the points. Use the line to estimate the cost of 8 gallons of gasoline.

3. **Open-Ended** Draw two line segments that start at the point $(2, -3)$ and have a length of 4 units. What are the endpoints of the two segments?

4. **Gridded Answer** You want to buy gifts for 3 friends while on vacation. For each friend, you decide to buy a shirt that costs $11.75, a necklace that costs $5.35, and a bookmark that costs $2. How much money do you spend on gifts for your friends?

5. **Short Response** A school marching band is selling pepperoni pizzas at a fair. The fair charges $30 to rent a stand. The band pays $4.25 for each plain pizza. The cost for the band to add pepperoni is $0.75 per pizza. Given that profit is the difference of income and expenses, write and simplify an expression for the band's profit from selling x pepperoni pizzas at $8 each. Show your work.

6. **Extended Response** You are planning a field trip to a science center. The cost for the bus is $120. Admission is $7 per person and lunch is $4 per person.

   a. Write two expressions for the total cost of taking x students.

   b. What would the cost be if 15 students went on the field trip? 20 students?

   c. Did you use the distributive property to find your answers in part (b)? *Explain* why or why not.

7. **Short Response** Plot the points $A(-3, -4)$, $B(-3, 2)$, $C(-1, 2)$, $D(-1, 5)$, $E(4, 5)$, and $F(4, -4)$ in a coordinate plane. Connect the points. Find the perimeter of the figure formed. Move the figure 3 units to the right. Write the new coordinates for the points.

Name _____ Date _____

Challenge Practice

For use with pages 94–100

In Exercises 1–5, identify the quadrant(s) in which the point lies with the described coordinates.

1. (a negative integer, the integer squared)

2. (a positive integer, the opposite of the absolute value of the integer)

3. (any integer, the integer cubed)

4. (any integer, the absolute value of the integer)

5. (any integer, the opposite of the integer)

In Exercises 6–8, use the following information. The points (−1, 3) and (2, 0) are two non-adjacent vertices of a square.

6. Plot the points on the given coordinate grid.

7. Give the coordinates of the two other vertices of the square. Then plot and connect the points.

8. Can you identify a set of coordinates in the first quadrant that could be the vertices of another square containing the points (−1, 3) and (2, 0)? Plot and connect the points with dotted lines.

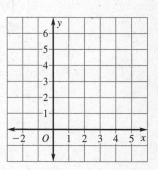

9. Complete the table of values. Then plot and connect the points.

x	$y = \lvert x \rvert - 4$	Ordered Pair
−3	$y = \lvert -3 \rvert - 4 = 3 - 4 = -1$	(−3, −1)
−2	_____	_____
−1	_____	_____
0	_____	_____
1	_____	_____
2	_____	_____
3	_____	_____

Name _____ Date _____

Games Support Master

For use with page 100

Spatial Delivery

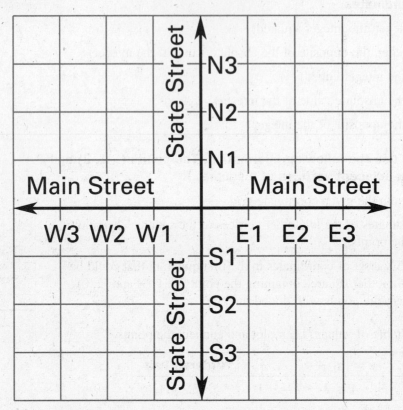

Name _____ Date _____

Chapter Review Games and Activities
For use after Chapter 2

Having Fun with the Coordinate Plane

Each exercise has two parts, **a** and **b**. The solutions to **a** and **b** represent an ordered pair, (a, b). Plot the ordered pair on the coordinate plane. Use a ruler to connect the points in order.

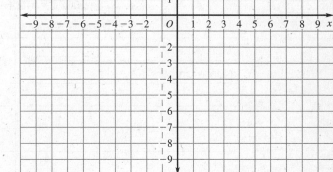

Simplify the expression.

1. **a.** $|-2|$ **b.** $-(-4)$

2. **a.** $-(-5)$ **b.** $|-5|$

Find the sum or difference.

3. **a.** $4 + (-1.5)$ **b.** $-5 + 7.5$

4. **a.** $-4 + 13$ **b.** $7 + (-7)$

Find the product or quotient.

5. **a.** $-2(-2)$ **b.** $\dfrac{-18}{9}$ 6. **a.** $\dfrac{-25}{-5}$ **b.** $5(-1)$

Evaluate the expression when $x = 2$, $y = -6$, and $z = 10$.

7. **a.** $y + z - x$ **b.** $4y + xz$ 8. **a.** $z + y - 2x$ **b.** $4y + z + 2x + 1$

Find the mean of the data.

9. **a.** $-2, 4, -7, -3$ 10. **a.** $6, -17, 1, -13, -2$

     b. $-11, -2, 5, -8$ **b.** $-9, 3, -10, 7, -16$

Evaluate the expression.

11. **a.** $4\left(-\dfrac{1}{2}\right) + \left(-\dfrac{1}{2}\right)$ 12. **a.** $(3 + 6)(-1)$

     b. $(-9.5 + 3) + 4$ **b.** $(2 + (-7))(0)$

13. Plot and continue connecting, in order, the following points.

     $(-4, 2), (-5, 5), (-2.5, 2.5), (0, 9), (2, 4)$

Shade in the triangle formed by connecting the set of 3 points.

14. $(0, 9), (0, 0), (2.5, 2.5)$ 15. $(5, 5), (2.5, 2.5), (4, 2)$

16. $(9, 0), (2.5, -2.5), (0, 0)$ 17. $(5, -5), (2, -4), (2.5, -2.5)$

18. $(0, -9), (0, 0), (-2.5, -2.5)$ 19. $(-5, -5), (-2.5, -2.5), (-4, -2)$

20. $(-9, 0), (0, 0), (-2.5, 2.5)$ 21. $(-5, 5), (-2.5, 2.5), (-2, 4)$

Review and Projects

Name _____ Date _____

Real-Life Project:
Make a Report Form

For use after Chapter 2

Objective Make and use daily report forms to keep track of daily data and find daily totals.

Materials paper, pencil

Investigation A local wildlife zoo uses a report form like the one shown below to keep track of the expenses and revenues of the Zoo Train.

ZOO TRAIN MONEY REPORT			
	Ticket Sales		**$ Amounts**
Members	_____	× $1 per rider =	_____
Non-Members	_____	× $3 per rider =	_____
		Total Sales	_____
		Less Refunds	_____
		Less Coupons	_____
		Less Misc.	_____
		Total Daily Profit	_____

In Exercises 1–3, copy the report form above and use it with the given information to find the profit for the day.

1. There were 255 non-members and 315 members who rode the train. There were 48 free train ride coupons used (by non-members only). There were no refunds or miscellaneous expenses.

2. There were 23 members and 12 non-members who rode the train. No coupons were used. A refund was given for a group of 68 members who purchased train tickets on the previous day, but were unable to ride because of a storm. There were no miscellaneous expenses.

3. There were 124 members and 93 non-members who rode the train. Fifty gallons of fuel mixture were purchased at $2 per gallon. The total cost of the fuel was a miscellaneous expense. There were refunds given to 22 members and 18 non-members when the train broke down.

4. Choose a business or situation that could use a report form to keep track of daily dollar amounts or some other type of amounts. Design a report form that could be used to keep track of the amounts. Do research to decide what categories to use in your report form. There should be categories for positive, as well as negative, integer amounts. Once you have made your form, use it to make a daily report based on a day's data from an actual business or situation of the type you have chosen. Document your source.

Teacher's Notes for Make a Report Form Project

For use after Chapter 2

Project Goals
- Add, subtract, multiply, or divide integers.
- Choose appropriate categories to organize real-life integer data.

Managing the Project
Guiding Students' Work You could suggest examples of situations to your students to get them going. You should monitor your students to see that they are making progress. You could set deadlines for things like choosing a situation, finding actual data, and so on. You may need to work with students to help them decide what data from the business or situation is pertinent and should be given categories in the report form. You may need to tell the students to round decimal amounts to integers for the project.

Classroom Management You could give the students class time at the library or on the Internet to do research.

Rubric for Project
The following rubric can be used to assess student work.

4 The student accurately calculates the daily totals for the Zoo Train. The student chooses an appropriate situation that has positive and negative categories to be accounted for. The student designs a sound report form to keep track of pertinent data. The student documents the research source. The student makes an accurate daily report based on actual data. The student documents the source(s).

3 The student accurately calculates the daily totals for the Zoo Train. The student chooses an appropriate situation. The student designs a mostly adequate report form, but may not account for all pertinent data. The student makes an actual daily report that is mostly accurate. The student documents the source(s).

2 The student may make an error or two in calculating the daily totals for the Zoo Train. The student chooses a situation that may not be completely adequate for the given task and may not have negative categories to be accounted for. The report form designed does not keep track of all pertinent data or may not be based on actual research. The student's actual daily report is not very accurate or is not based on research. The student does not adequately document research sources.

1 The student makes errors in calculating totals for the Zoo Train and using the report form. The student puts little effort into choosing an appropriate situation. The student's report form represents the situation poorly. The student does not use real data to make an actual daily report. The student does not accurately document any research sources.

Review and Projects

Cooperative Project:
Integer Chip Game

For use after Chapter 2

Objective   Make and play a game to practice integer operations.

Materials   index cards, markers, blue chips, red chips, calculator

Inestigation   The integer chip game is a review game designed to practice the four basic integer operations. The game is played by 2 or more people.

Setting up the game

- Each player uses index cards to create 16 flash cards by writing an integer expression on each card. Make 4 cards for each operation: addition, subtraction, multiplication, and division.

- Shuffle the cards of all the players together and place them in a pile, face down.

- Blue chips are worth 2 points. Red chips count as a -1 point. Players start the game without chips. Chips are given as the game is played.

Playing the game

- A player draws the top card and simplifies the expression.

- One at a time, following the order of upcoming player turns, the opponents are given an opportunity to challenge the answer. If an opponent disagrees with the player's answer, the opponent challenges and gives what he or she thinks is the correct answer. A calculator is then used to find the correct answer. If the correct answer is the same as one of the 2 given answers, the player who gave that answer receives a blue chip. A red chip is given to one or both players who answered incorrectly. The next player then starts a turn.

- If no opponents make a challenge, the player who drew the card and simplified the expression receives a blue chip and the next player starts the turn.

- The game continues until time runs out or all the cards have been used.

- The winner is the person who has the greatest score, determined by adding the values of the red and blue chips together at the end of the game.

1. Two players play one-on-one. One player ends up with 10 blue chips and 8 red chips, and the other player with 22 blue chips and 2 red chips. What is the final score?

2. What is the greatest possible difference of the scores of two opponents playing one-on-one if a total of 32 cards are drawn?

3. Create your own game that reviews the operations for integers. Tell how the game should be set up and give the rules for playing the game. Be sure to review all of the rules to your game. Check that someone else would be able to follow the rules and be able to play the game.

Teacher's Notes for Integer Chip Game Project

For use after Chapter 2

Project Goals
- Add, subtract, multiply and divide integers.
- Write integer expressions using the four basic operations.

Managing the Project

Guiding Students' Work You should check the flash card expressions after they are written to ensure appropriateness. Encourage students to write questions that are a variety of difficulty levels. Go over the rules of the game with your students to prevent confusion while they are playing the game. The students will need strong guidance for designing their own game logistically.

Classroom Management You might consider grouping students according to ability level. This will help make the games less one-sided. At lower skill levels, you might consider using teams of two rather than individual play. This allows cooperative discussion between teammates. No more than 2 students on a team are recommended.

Rubric for Project

The following rubric can be used to assess student work.

4 Integer expressions on flash cards are written appropriately. The integer chip game is set up and played correctly. Questions 1 and 2 are correctly answered. The students create a game using all four of the integer operations. The game setup and rules are appropriately described. The game works logistically.

3 Integer expressions on flash cards are written appropriately. The integer chip game is set up and played with few problems. Questions 1 and 2 are correctly answered. The students create a review game that may or may not include all four operations. The game setup and rules are described, but may not be logistically sound enough to play the game.

2 Some integer expressions on the flash cards may not have been written appropriately without guidance. The students needed some guidance to play the game. Questions 1 and 2 are answered, but may not both be correct. The students make an attempt to design a review game, but the setup and rules are not explained sufficiently for the game to be played.

1 The students need excessive guidance to set up and play the integer chip game. Questions 1 and 2 are both answered wrong, with little or no work shown. An idea is presented for a game, but little or no attempt is made to organize and detail the setup and rules.

Name _____ Date _____

Independent Extra Credit Project: Review Poster

For use after Chapter 2

Objective   Make review posters to review the integer operations.

Materials   poster paper, markers

Investigation   In this project you will make 5 posters to review the operations with integers.

Include the following information in each poster.

Poster 1: Detailed procedures for adding integers
  Examples and solutions for:
    Adding 2 negative integers
    Adding a positive integer to a negative integer
    Adding a negative integer to a positive integer

Poster 2: Detailed procedures for subtracting integers
  Examples and solutions for:
    Subtracting a negative integer from a negative integer
    Subtracting a positive integer from a negative integer
    Subtracting a negative integer from a positive integer

Poster 3: Detailed procedures for multiplying integers
  Examples and solutions for:
    Multiplying a negative integer by a negative integer
    Multiplying a positive integer by a negative integer
    Multiplying a negative integer by a positive integer

Poster 4: Detailed procedures for dividing integers
  Examples and solutions for:
    Dividing a negative integer by a negative integer
    Dividing a positive integer by a negative integer
    Dividing a negative integer by a positive integer

Poster 5: A statement of the order of operations
  An example and evaluation of an expression that requires using the
  order of operations. The expression should have at least one instance
  of each basic operation, at least 3 negative integers, and at least one
  expression within grouping symbols.
  An example and solution that shows how the distributive property
  could be used as an exception to the order of operations for a certain
  type of expression with grouping symbols.

Each poster should be neat, organized, easy to read, and have a title. Make sure
a complete set of procedures is given for each operation, with all the information
necessary to perform the operation with *any* two integers.

Review and Projects

Teacher's Notes for Review
Poster Project

For use after Chapter 2

Project Goals
- Add, subtract, multiply, and divide integers.
- Evaluate expressions by using the correct order of operations.
- Use the distributive property.

Managing the Project

Guiding Students' Work Reassert that your students should include detailed steps for all the procedures necessary to perform each operation with any two integers. Stress that the students include all of the required examples for each poster. Give some guidance for how to organize the project so your students can make posters that are neat and easy to read. On poster 5, you *may* or *may not* suggest that the students use the same expression for the distributive property example as for the order of operations example, to show how the two procedures compare.

Rubric for Project

The following rubric can be used to assess student work.

4 The student makes review posters that contain detailed procedures for adding, subtracting, multiplying, dividing, and performing the correct order of operations. The posters have all required examples and correct solutions. The student aptly shows how the use of the distributive property can change order of operations slightly. The posters are neat, organized, easy to read, and titled.

3 The student makes review posters that contain the correct and complete procedures for adding, subtracting, multiplying, dividing, and performing the correct order of operations. All of the required examples are included, but there may be a couple of errors in the solutions. The student may not have clearly shown how use of the distributive property can differ from the normal order of operations. The posters are fairly neat, organized, easy to read, and have titles.

2 The student makes posters with procedures for adding, subtracting, multiplying, dividing, and performing the order of operations, but some procedures may not be complete and/or correct. The student may not have included all of the required examples. There are errors in some of the student's examples. The student probably has not adequately compared use of the distributive property to the order of operations. The posters have titles but are probably not well organized or very neat.

1 The student either fails to make all 5 posters or fails to include many of the required examples. Many procedures are incomplete and wrong. There are many errors in the included examples. The student does not have a comparison of the distributive property to the normal order of operations. The posters are disorganized and messy. They may not have titles.

Review and Projects

In Exercises 1–3, use the bar graph at the right. It shows the percent of weekly Internet use for each age group. (Lesson 1.1)

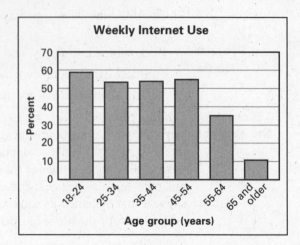

1. Which age group has the greatest percent of people accessing the Internet?

2. Which age group has the lowest percent of people accessing the Internet?

3. Out of 100 people, about how many more 18 to 24 year olds access the Internet than people 65 years old and older?

Evaluate the expression. (Lessons 1.2, 1.4)

4. $10 + 6 - 4$

5. $3 + 9 \div 3$

6. $8 + 3 \cdot (7 - 5)$

7. $5 \cdot 2^3 - 15$

8. $(5 - 2)^3 - 1 + 4^2$

9. $32 \div (9 - 7)^4$

Write the phrase as a variable expression. Let x represent the variable. (Lesson 1.3)

10. 21 decreased by a number

11. seven times a number

12. 4 more than a number

13. 6 less than a number

Solve the equation using mental math. (Lesson 1.5)

14. $12 - w = 8$

15. $s \div 6 = 5$

16. $x + 7 = 10$

17. $6y = 48$

18. $24 \div n = 2$

19. $t - 8 = 20$

Find the perimeter and area of the rectangle or square. (Lesson 1.6)

20.
9 cm

3 cm

21.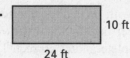
10 ft

24 ft

22.
6 in.

6 in.

23. You had $125 in your savings account. During the past six months you have deposited $15 in your account five times and have withdrawn $20 from your account twice. What is the new balance in your account? (Lesson 1.7)

Name _____ Date _____

Cumulative Practice
For use after Chapter 2

Complete the statement with <, >, or =. (Lesson 2.1)

24. 12 ____ -6 **25.** -5 ____ 1 **26.** 0 ____ -3

27. -4 ____ -9 **28.** $|-7|$ ____ 7 **29.** $|8|$ ____ 8

Find the sum, difference, product, or quotient. (Lessons 2.2–2.5)

30. $-35 + 13$ **31.** $20 + (-11)$ **32.** $-15 + (-27)$

33. $14 - 21$ **34.** $16 - (-17)$ **35.** $-30 - 12$

36. $-8(-7)$ **37.** $4(-12)$ **38.** $-7(3)$

39. $\dfrac{-36}{4}$ **40.** $\dfrac{-24}{-8}$ **41.** $\dfrac{0}{-15}$

Use the properties of addition and multiplication to find the missing number or variable. Name the property. (Lesson 2.6)

42. $-25 +$ ____ $= -25$ **43.** $(x + 4) + 8 = x + ($ ____ $+ 8)$

44. $-7 + y =$ ____ $+ (-7)$ **45.** $17 \cdot$ ____ $= 17$

Simplify the expression by combining like terms. (Lesson 2.7)

46. $7c + 14d + d - 5c$ **47.** $-4x + 11 - 6x - 5$

48. $9y + 6 + 4y - 2x$ **49.** $u + u - 4 - 3u + 1$

Use the distributive property to simplify the expression. (Lesson 2.7)

50. $5(x + 4)$ **51.** $6(y - 1)$ **52.** $9(7 + 4)$

53. $-3(-8 + 4)$ **54.** $-8(t + 2)$ **55.** $-6(u + v - 3)$

Give the coordinates of the point. (Lesson 2.8)

56. A **57.** B

58. C **59.** D

60. E **61.** F

Plot the point in the coordinate plane and describe its location. (Lesson 2.8)

62. $(-2, 6)$ **63.** $(4, -1)$

64. $(0, 3)$ **65.** $(-1, -4)$

66. $(-5, 0)$ **67.** $(2, 5)$

Review and Projects

Name _____ Date _____

Problem Solving Workshop:
Gridded Answer Sheet

For use with Mixed Problem Solving for 2.1–2.5 and 2.6–2.8

Answers

Lesson 2.1

Teaching Guide

1. $-7, -5, -1, 0, 2, 4, 6$
2. $-4, 5, 0, -2, 7, 1, -6$
3. $-6, -4, -2, 0, 1, 5, 7$ 4. 1.71

Practice A

1. integers 2. less 3. greater 4. the number; zero 5. opposites 6. $-10, -9, -5, -3, 1, 4, 6, 7$
7. $-36, -21, -4, 0, 3, 7, 14$ 8. $-42, -38, -34, -18, 10, 38$ 9. $-24, -15, -4, -1, 0, 5, 17, 24$ 10. $-12; 12$ 11. $4; 4$ 12. $-3; 3$ 13. $15; 15$ 14. $<$ 15. $>$ 16. $<$ 17. $<$ 18. $>$ 19. $>$ 20. E
21. D 22. C 23. A 24. B 25. 8 26. 4
27. -14 28. -9 29. -3 30. -10 31. $|-282|$

Practice B

1. negative 2. positive 3. $-24, -16, -8, 2, 7, 17, 23$ 4. $-136, -56, -38, -24, -16, 11, 25, 102$ 5. $-10, -7, -5, -1, 0, 2, 4, 6$ 6. $-84, -51, -39, -15, 8, 17, 73$ 7. $-7; 7$ 8. $25; 25$
9. $-106; 106$ 10. $241; 241$ 11. $<$ 12. $>$
13. $<$ 14. $<$ 15. $>$ 16. $>$ 17. E 18. D
19. C 20. A 21. B 22. 15 23. 9 24. 16
25. -6 26. 49 27. -34 28. Juanita 29. Sarah
30. Juanita, Beth, Tamika, Sarah, Ingrid

Practice C

1. $-7, -5, -1, 0, 1, 3, 4, 6$ 2. $-45, -31, -29, -17, 28, 34, 67$ 3. $-104, -91, -88, -73, -27, 41, 53, 59$ 4. $-716, -506, -463, -214, 190, 246, 308, 459$ 5. $44; 44$ 6. $-85; 85$ 7. $137; 137$ 8. $-2461; 2461$ 9. $>$ 10. $>$ 11. $<$ 12. $<$
13. $>$ 14. $>$ 15. $-(-14)$ 16. $|14|$ 17. $-|-14|$
18. $|-14|$ 19. $-|14|$ 20. 13 21. 21 22. -17
23. -43 24. 58 25. -37
26. $-(-106), |24|, -|-16|, -34, -|-81|$
27. $-(-31), |-15|, -|-26|, -|72|, -85$
28. $-(-34), |-31|, -|36|, -|39|, -43$
29. $63, -(-55), (-|-49|), -(51), -[-(-73)]$
30. Dead Sea shore 31. -1312 ft, -512 ft, -138 ft, $19,340$ ft, $29,035$ ft 32. Lake Assal

Study Guide

1. $-8, -2, 0, 5, 6$ 2. $-12, -6, 3, 9, 15$
3. $-7, -4, 0, 4, 16$ 4. $-7, -5, -4, -3, 2$
5. -7 6. 1 7. $-\frac{1}{2}$ 8. -2 9. -62 10. -26.5
11. $>$ 12. $<$ 13. $<$ 14. $<$ 15. $>$ 16. $>$

Real-World Problem Solving

1. May 2. July 3. 11 inches 4. July, August, June, September, October, March, April, May

Challenge Practice

1. sometimes; $-(10) = -10$, but $-(-10) = 10$
2. sometimes; $|-4| > -4$ but $|4| = 4$ 3. never; The absolute value of an integer is always positive, and the opposite of a positive integer is negative.
4. sometimes; $-(6) = -6$ and $|6| = 6$, but $-(-6) = 6 = |6|$ 5. always; $-(-(5)) = 5$; $-(-(-5)) = -5$ 6. *Sample Answer:* $x = 4$ and $y = 5$ 7. *Sample Answer:* $x = 0, y = 0; x = 4, y = -4; x = 5, y = -5$ 8. x and y are opposites.

Lesson 2.2

Teaching Guide

1. Yes, 0 is an integer. 2. The absolute value of a number is the distance the number is from 0 on a number line.
3. No, if $a = -6$ and $b = 2, a > b$.

Practice A

1. $-6 + 11; 5$ 2. 2 3. -1 4. -9
5. absolute values 6. subtract; sign 7. 8
8. -47 9. -92 10. -170 11. -23 12. -29
13. 21 14. -56 15. -66 16. $-12 + 6$; $6°$ below zero 17. 9 feet below the surface of the water 18. -19 19. 20 20. -65 21. -15
22. no; she still needs $7

Practice B

1. $-4 + 11; 7$ 2. 1 3. -5 4. -9 5. 9
6. -17 7. -97 8. -7 9. 9 10. -41
11. -43 12. -68 13. -121 14. never
15. never 16. never 17. sometimes 18. -13

Lesson 2.2 *continued*

19. −9 **20.** −30 **21.** −140 **22.** $227
23. 2 seconds

Practice C

1. 4 **2.** −7 **3.** −17 **4.** −22 **5.** −27 **6.** −104
7. 38 **8.** −46 **9.** −49 **10.** −166 **11.** −77
12. −366 **13.** sometimes **14.** always **15.** never
16. never **17.** −4 **18.** −1 **19.** −42 **20.** 124
21. 314 **22.** −1237 **23.** 167 **24.** −1388 **25.** yes
26. 6 **27.** −5 **28.** −12 **29.** 2 **30.** 26,710 ft;
23,839 ft **31.** no; no; yes; yes; If *a* and *b* have
different signs then *a* and the opposite of *b* are
both negative or both positive and the expressions
are equal. If *a* and *b* have the same signs then
the opposite of *b* has a different sign and the
expressions are not equal.

Study Guide

1. −3 **2.** −13 **3.** −3 **4.** 4 **5.** −1 **6.** 0 **7.** −6
8. 6 **9.** −17 **10.** 15 **11.** 492 **12.** 217
13. −34

Challenge Practice

1. 4, −10 **2.** −8, 16 **3.** 4, 6 **4.** −12, −8
5. −2, 18 **6.** 5, −13 **7.** $12 + (−4) + (−6); 2$
8. $−3 + 10 + 20; 27$ **9.** $−2 + (−18) + 11;$
$−9$ **10.** $14 + (−3) + 5 + (−12); 4$

Lesson 2.3

Teaching Guide

1. $155 **2.** $100 **3.** 3 days

Practice A

1. $a; (−b)$ **2.** $a; b$ **3.** D **4.** A **5.** B **6.** C
7. −3 **8.** −7 **9.** 7 **10.** −30 **11.** 3 **12.** 2
13. 0 **14.** −15 **15.** −22 **16.** −17 **17.** −13
18. 7 **19.** $−7 − 12; −19$ **20.** $13 − (−4); 17$
21. $−9 − (−15); 6$ **22.** 10 **23.** −22 **24.** 4
25. −31°F **26.** −$61 **27.** −169 **28.** −132
29. 593 **30.** 4 **31.** −11 **32.** −5 **33.** 30
34. −47 **35.** −26

Practice B

1. −4 **2.** −15 **3.** 7 **4.** −21 **5.** −5 **6.** −3
7. 40 **8.** −14 **9.** −16 **10.** −11 **11.** −12
12. −95 **13.** $−6 − 19; −25$ **14.** $8 − (−21); 29$
15. $−15 − (−28); 13$ **16.** 10 **17.** −28 **18.** −29
19. $483 **20.** 47 ft **21.** −247 **22.** −75 **23.** 846
24. 3 **25.** −12 **26.** −24 **27.** −1 **28.** −8
29. −88 **30.** −31 **31.** 15 **32.** 9 **33.** −10
34. −12 **35.** −9 **36.** d **37.** It went down
67 cents.

Practice C

1. −8 **2.** −27 **3.** 4 **4.** −28 **5.** 2 **6.** 18 **7.** −8
8. 64 **9.** 6 **10.** −80 **11.** −13 **12.** −31
13. $16 − (−24); 40$ **14.** $−26 − (−31); 5$
15. −24 **16.** 12 **17.** −57 **18.** Subtract the lesser
value from the greater value: $146 − (−174)$
19. 980 ft **20.** 1640 ft **21.** 650 ft **22.** −367
23. 17 **24.** 433 **25.** 11 **26.** −20 **27.** −230
28. −4 **29.** −54 **30.** −219 **31.** −49 **32.** 30
33. 5

Study Guide

1. −6 **2.** −25 **3.** 72 **4.** 40 **5.** −123 **6.** 87
7. −3 **8.** −42 **9.** −2 **10.** −1 **11.** −18
12. 18 **13.** 12 **14.** −1 **15.** $18 **16.** $7

Challenge Practice

1. 2, 10 **2.** 1, 3 **3.** −6, 24 **4.** −6, 14
5. positive **6.** negative **7.** negative
8. *Sample Answer:* $x = 2, y = 4$
9. *Sample Answer:* $x = 0, y = 0$ and $x = 4,$
$y = 2$ **10.** yes; no

Lesson 2.4

Teaching Guide

1. $48 **2.** $54 **3.** $102 **4.** $75

Activity Master

1. The product of a positive integer and a
negative integer is negative. **2.** −9 **3.** −12
4. −15 **5.** −18 **6.** −6; −4; −2; 0; 2; 4

Lesson 2.4 continued

7. The product of two negative integers is positive.

Practice A

1. C **2.** B **3.** D **4.** A **5.** −24 **6.** 42 **7.** 0
8. −50 **9.** 33 **10.** 156 **11.** −98 **12.** −152
13. −240 **14.** 64 **15.** 432 **16.** −147 **17.** 160
18. 168 **19.** 43 **20.** 7 **21.** −1080 **22.** −72
23. 21 **24.** −90 **25.** 135 **26.** −5 **27.** 7 **28.** −7
29. $30 **30.** 45 plants **31.** $220 **32.** −24 pounds

Practice B

1. −36 **2.** 35 **3.** 0 **4.** 99 **5.** −96 **6.** 260
7. −306 **8.** 288 **9.** −210 **10.** 792 **11.** 0
12. −455 **13.** 126 **14.** −462 **15.** 113 **16.** 30
17. −4851 **18.** −378 **19.** 48 **20.** −63 **21.** 160
22. −7 **23.** 3 **24.** −5 **25.** 15 bundles **26.** the
17-yard line **27.** −78 **28.** 6084 **29.** 8281
30. 23 steps behind the original position **31.** $132

Practice C

1. −45 **2.** 77 **3.** 0 **4.** −120 **5.** −224 **6.** 285
7. −483 **8.** −96 **9.** 420 **10.** −1170 **11.** 0
12. 896 **13.** 1144 **14.** −1456 **15.** 263 **16.** 63
17. 6864 **18.** −583 **19.** 105 **20.** −72 **21.** 297
22. −8 **23.** 3 **24.** −2 **25.** $640 **26.** $586,500
27. −31,752 **28.** −28,098 **29.** 15,876
30. −32,634 **31.** −5292 **32.** 10,206 **33.** −1
34. 0 **35.** −1 **36.** n must be odd.
37. n must be even.

Study Guide

1. 100 miles **2.** $225 **3.** −30 **4.** 12 **5.** 77
6. 0 **7.** 24 **8.** 0 **9.** −48 **10.** −56 **11.** 3
12. −9 **13.** −5 **14.** −23

Challenge Practice

1. Row 8: 8, 14, 18, 20, 20, 18, 14, 8;
Row 9: 9, 16, 21, 24, 25, 24, 21, 16, 9
2. 6; 9; n **3.** 1, 4, 9, 16, 25; 36; 49
4. Row 14: 14, 26, 36, 44, 50, 54, 56, 56, 54,
50, 44, 36, 26, 14 **5.** > **6.** < **7.** <

Lesson 2.5

Teaching Guide

1. $720 **2.** 8 weeks **3.** $90 **4.** It will decrease
the average weekly cost becasue you are now
adding a number lower than the average.

Practice A

1. false **2.** true **3.** true **4.** false **5.** −5 **6.** 7
7. −7 **8.** −5 **9.** 0 **10.** −8 **11.** −4 **12.** 4
13. 9 **14.** undefined **15.** −3 **16.** −8 **17.** −2
18. −4 **19.** −4 **20.** 6 **21.** −16 **22.** 4 **23.** 0
24. −3 **25.** −2 **26.** 2 **27.** −8°F **28.** −1 pound

Practice B

1. 8 **2.** −8 **3.** −5 **4.** 0 **5.** undefined **6.** −12
7. −2 **8.** −8 **9.** −9 **10.** 8 **11.** −21 **12.** 5
13. 4 **14.** −3 **15.** −2 **16.** −48 **17.** −6
18. 6 **19.** 4 **20.** −5 **21.** −6 **22.** 3 **23.** −6
24. Woods: 276; Goosen: 279; Mickelson: 280;
Olazabal: 281; Harrington, Els: 282; Singh: 283,
Garcia: 284; Jimenez, Scott, Cabrera: 285
25. 282 **26.** 282; The numbers are the same.

Practice C

1. −4 **2.** 7 **3.** −6 **4.** −15 **5.** −6 **6.** −12
7. 0 **8.** 9 **9.** undefined **10.** 43 **11.** −41
12. 15 **13.** 3 **14.** −288 **15.** −96 **16.** 4
17. −32 **18.** 2 **19.** 2 **20.** −3 **21.** −7 **22.** 5
23. −2.4 **24.** 1.2 **25.** −0.0625 **26.** −3.2 yd
27. −$2700

Study Guide

1. 58 **2.** −19 **3.** −12 **4.** −8 **5.** 0 **6.** −1 **7.** 9
8. 0 **9.** −7 **10.** 2 **11.** $\frac{1}{8}$ **12.** −1 **13.** $-\frac{1}{4}$

Answers

Problem Solving Workshop: Mixed Problem Solving

1. a. April, June, July **b.** −200, 200, −300, 400, 400 **c.** $500 **2. a.** 36, 0, −44 **b.** At 2 seconds the ball is 36 feet above the ground and 64 feet from the top of the building. At 2.5 seconds, the ball is on the ground and 100 feet from the top of the building. At 3 seconds, the value from the function does not make sense. The ball will not be 44 feet below the ground. At 3 seconds, the ball will be on the ground and 100 feet from the top of the building. **3.** 8 **4.** −3.4°F; The mean would increase to −2.4°F because you are adding 5 to the total and dividing the total by 5.

5. a. 6095 points **b.** 404 games
c. Abdul-Jabbar: 24.6, Malone: 25.0, Jordan: 30.1; Michael Jordan had the highest career points per game average. He averaged 5.1 more points per game than Karl Malone and 5.5 more points per game than Kareem Abdul-Jabbar.

Real-World Problem Solving

1.

	Mon	Tues	Wed	Thurs
k 1	57	62	59	55
k 2	52	50	48	51
Change	−5	−12	−11	−4
k 3	42	45	43	39
Overall Change	−15	−17	−16	−16
k 4	36	38	39	34
Overall Change	−21	−24	−20	−21

	Fri	Sat	Sun	Average for Week
k 1	58	61	54	58 mi/h
k 2	49	47	53	50 mi/h
Change	−9	−14	−1	−8 mi/h
k 3	38	40	36	40.43 mi/h
Overall Change	−20	−21	−18	−17.57 mi/h
k 4	35	37	35	36.29 mi/h
Overall Change	−23	−24	−19	−21.71 mi/h

2. 21.71 mi/h **3.** yes

Challenge Practice

1. geometric; −1 **2.** not geometric **3.** not geometric **4.** geometric; $-\frac{1}{3}$ **5.** −2, 6, −18, 54, −162 **6.** 10, −40, 160, −640, 2560 **7.** −1000, −100, −10, −1, −0.1 **8.** $-\frac{1}{8}, \frac{1}{4}, -\frac{1}{2}, 1, -2$
9. 320; −2560 **10.** $5(-2)^{n-1}$

Lesson 2.6

Teaching Guide

1. $128 **2.** $125 **3.** $587

Practice A

1. B **2.** D **3.** C **4.** A **5.** 3; Associative Property of Addition **6.** 5; Commutative Property of Multiplication **7.** 7; Associative Property of Multiplication **8.** 5; Commutative Property of Addition **9.** 53 **10.** −26 **11.** 27 **12.** 79
13. −5082 **14.** −700 **15.** −165 **16.** 68 **17.** 259
18. $-32x$ **19.** $8 + x$ **20.** $109 + x$ **21.** increased by $210 **22.** $290 **23.** 7.1 **24.** 210 **25.** 729
26. $3\frac{1}{2}$ **27.** −228 **28.** 195 **29.** 314 cm

Practice B

1. b; a **2.** b; a **3.** a; b; c **4.** a; b; c
5. 5; Associative Property of Addition **6.** 12; Commutative Property of Multiplication **7.** 5; Associative Property of Multiplication **8.** 51; Commutative Property of Addition
9. 69 **10.** −52 **11.** −2 **12.** 21 **13.** −65
14. 78,000 **15.** −130 **16.** 900 **17.** 88
18. $-90x$ **19.** $x - 64$ **20.** $x + 93$ **21.** $x - 47$
22. $x + 3$ **23.** $357x$ **24.** 4 cups
25. 36 miles north **26.** 5.5 **27.** 720 **28.** 81
29. $2\frac{2}{5}$ **30.** −65 **31.** 66

Practice C

1. 15; Associative Property of Addition **2.** 18; Commutative Property of Multiplication **3.** 22; Associative Property of Multiplication **4.** 42; Commutative Property of Addition
5. 3 **6.** −136 **7.** −2160 **8.** −89 **9.** −11

10. 1800 **11.** -153 **12.** -112 **13.** 736
14. $-96x$ **15.** $x - 118$ **16.** $x + 89$ **17.** $x - 66$
18. $x + 98$ **19.** $435x$ **20.** 18 forks **21.** $252.00
22. 4 **23.** 327 **24.** 220 **25.** $6\frac{1}{3}$ **26.** -84
27. 255 **28.** $9 \cdot 7 + 3$; $3 + 7 \cdot 9$; $7 \cdot 9 + 3$
29. $221.00

Study Guide

1. $600 **2.** $800 **3.** -120 **4.** -18 **5.** 9
6. -6600 **7.** 97 **8.** -64 **9.** 170 **10.** -4300
11. -700 **12.** 42 **13.** 30 **14.** 0

Problem Solving Workshop: Using Alternative Methods

1. No; After 6 days you have only biked 360 miles. **2.** 153 yards **3.** $105 **4.** $54

Challenge Practice

1. no; $24 \div (6 \div 2) = 8 \neq (24 \div 6) \div 2 = 2$
2. no; $8 - 5 = 3 \neq 5 - 8 = -3$
3. no; $8 - (5 - 1) = 4 \neq (8 - 5) - 1 = 2$
4. No; the order of the activities changes the outcome. **5.** Yes; the order of the activities does not change the outcome. **6.** Answers will vary.
7. Answers will vary.

Lesson 2.7

Teaching Guide

1. 3 games **2.** 3 juices; 3 slices of pizza
3. $3(3 + 1 + 1.25)$ **4.** $15.75

Practice A

1. B **2.** C **3.** A **4.** D **5.** $-6(4) + (-6)(3)$
6. $8(9) + 8(4)$ **7.** $2(6) + 2(7)$
8. $-4x + (-4)(3)$ **9.** $5(2) + 5x$ **10.** $6x - 6(3)$
11. $5m$ **12.** $10x + 7y$ **13.** $15m + 10p$
14. $6c + 7d$ **15.** $-3x - 16y$ **16.** $10x - 4y - 5$
17. $8(7 + 0.50)$ **18.** 56; 4 **19.** 60 **20.** 125 ft^2
21. 190 cm^2 **22.** $9w - 54$ **23.** $14x$ **24.** $12x - 3$
25. $37d$ **26.** p **27.** $23g - 39$

28. You can add to find that the cost of a sandwich and drink is $5. Multiplying by 4, you get a total of $20. **29.** 10,000 ft^2

Practice B

1. $-5y + (-5)(7)$ **2.** $4(11) + 4(6)$
3. $6(8) + 6m$ **4.** $-31(24) + (-31)(12)$
5. $13(7) + 13w + 13(-9)$
6. $-29p - (-29)(21) - (-29)(5)$ **7.** $9c + 5d$
8. $10m + 12k$ **9.** $13s + 4t$ **10.** $12c + 5d$
11. $-20g - 16h$ **12.** $19x + 3y$ **13.** 224 in.^{2}
14. 297 mm^2 **15.** $12w - 96$ **16.** $-33x$
17. $7x - 8$ **18.** $26d$ **19.** $10p$ **20.** $4g - 32$
21. Multiply the total cost of a necklace and earrings, $30, by 7. The total cost is $210.
22. $83.58 **23.** 105 **24.** 92 **25.** 216
26. 1560 **27.** $15(27 + 31)$; 870 ft^2

Practice C

1. $-9y + (-9)(6)$ **2.** $7(15) - 7(8)$
3. $5(7) + 5m + 5(13)$
4. $-12(4) + (-12)w + (-12)(-6)$
5. $-24p - (-24)(22) - (-24)(15)$
6. $35(21) + 35(17) + 35(3x)$ **7.** $12c + 7d$
8. $22m + 24k$ **9.** $22s + 2t$ **10.** $-5c + 4d$
11. $-30g + 4h$ **12.** $11x + 3y - 3$ **13.** 592 yd^2
14. 874 in.^{2} **15.** $15w - 180$ **16.** $-108x$
17. $x - 7$ **18.** $69d$ **19.** $29p$ **20.** $72 - 36g$
21. $18 **22.** $180 **23.** 152 **24.** 162 **25.** 156
26. 384 **27.** $5 + (20.25 + 3.5)x$; $598.75; $1192.50

Study Guide

1. 36 ft^2 **2.** 128 ft^2 **3.** -45 **4.** 168 **5.** -25
6. $2w - 18$ **7.** $-56 + 8y$ **8.** z **9.** $-4r$
10. $16w$ **11.** $3x - 6y$ **12.** $14r$

Challenge Practice

1. yes **2.** yes **3.** yes **4.** yes **5.** no **6.** no
7. yes **8.** yes

Lesson 2.8

Teaching Guide

1.
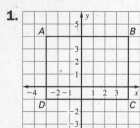

2. 24 units **3.** 35 square units **4.** 48 ft; 140 ft²

Technology Activity

1.

4 units left, 5 units
up from origin;
Quadrant II

2.
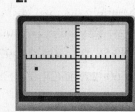

8 units left, 3 units
down from origin;
Quadrant III

3.
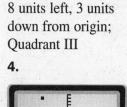

9 units right, 6 units
up from origin;
Quadrant I

4.

5 units left, 9 units
up from origin;
Quadrant II

5.

2 units right, 3 units
down from origin;
Quadrant IV

6.

4 units right, 3 units
up from origin;
Quadrant I

7.

7 units left, 8 units
down from origin;
Quadrant III

8.
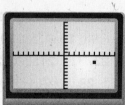

6 units right, 2 units
down from origin;
Quadrant IV

Practice A

1. H **2.** I **3.** C **4.** A **5.** F **6.** G **7.** B **8.** D
9. E **10.** (1, −2) **11.** (0, 2) **12.** (−2, 3)
13. (−3, −1) **14.** (−1, 0) **15.** (3, 1)

Graph for 16–21.

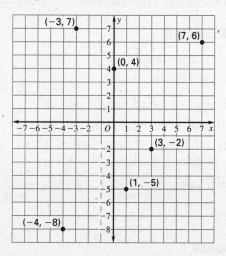

16. right 3, down 2 from origin, Quadrant IV

17. up 4 from origin, *y*-axis **18.** right 7, up 6
from origin, Quadrant I **19.** right 1, down 5 from
origin, Quadrant IV **20.** left 3, up 7 from origin,
Quadrant II **21.** left 4, down 8 from origin,
Quadrant III

22. rectangle; 10   **23.** rectangle; 18

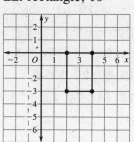   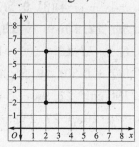

Lesson 2.8 continued

24. square; 16

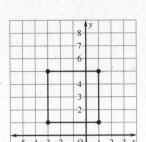

25–26. The points lie on a line.

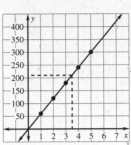

26. 210 miles

27. $P = 28$ units; $A = 48$ square units

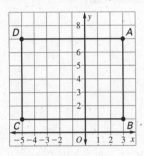

Practice B

1. $(6, -2)$ **2.** $(0, -3)$ **3.** $(-3, 1)$ **4.** $(1, 5)$

5. $(4, 0)$ **6.** $(3, -7)$

Graph for 7–12.

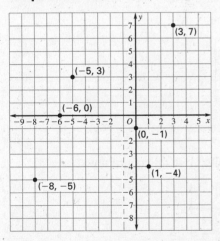

7. left 5, up 3 from origin, Quadrant II **8.** right 1, down 4 from origin, Quadrant IV **9.** down 1 from origin, y-axis **10.** right 3, up 7 from origin, Quadrant I **11.** left 6 from origin, x-axis **12.** left 8, down 5 from origin, Quadrant III

13. rectangle; 14

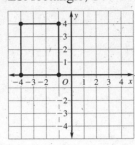

14. rectangle; 26

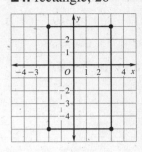

15. square; 20

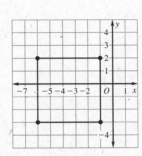

16. The points lie on a line.

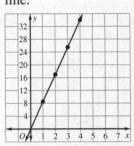

17. $51

18. $P = 26$ units; $A = 40$ square units

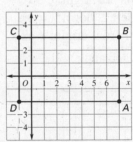

19. $P = 26$ units; $A = 42$ square units

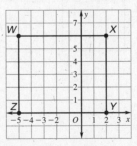

20. $P = 22$ units; $A = 30$ square units

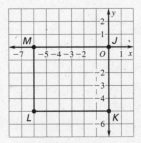

Lesson 2.8 continued

Practice C

1. $(-3, 4)$ **2.** $(9, -6)$ **3.** $(0, -7)$ **4.** $(-8, 0)$

5. $(4, 1)$ **6.** $(5, 7)$

Graph for 7–12.

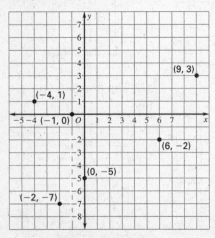

7. right 6, down 2 from origin; Quadrant IV

8. left 4, up 1 from origin; Quadrant II

9. down 5 from origin; y-axis **10.** right 9, up 3 from origin; Quadrant I **11.** left 2, down 7 from origin; Quadrant III **12.** left 1 from origin; x-axis

13. square;16   **14.** rectangle; 30

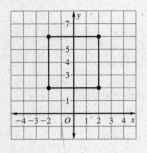   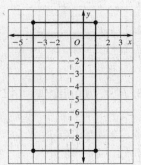

15. rectangle; 38

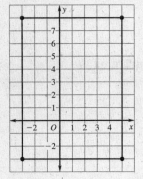

16. 7, 14, 21, 28

17–18.

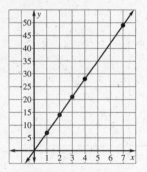

18. 49 minutes

19. $P = 38$ units; $A = 70$ square units

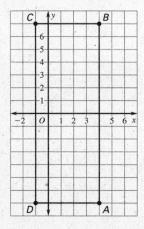

20. $P = 16$ units; $A = 15$ square units

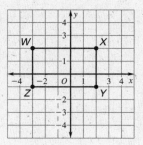

21. $P = 28$ units; $A = 48$ square units

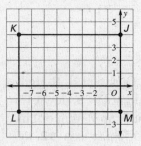

22. Rectangles will vary; The perimeter of the new rectangle is 3 times as great.

Lesson 2.8 *continued*

Study Guide

1. $D(2, 1)$ **2.** $E(-5, 2)$ **3.** $F(0, 4)$

4. Begin at the origin, move 10 units to the left, then 4 units up. Point R lies in Quadrant II.

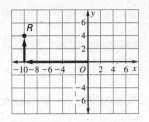

5. Begin at the origin, move 5 units to the right, then 8 units down. Point S lies in Quadrant IV.

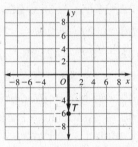

6. Begin at the origin, move 6 units down. Point T lies on the y-axis.

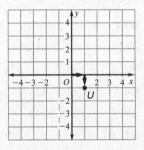

7. Begin at the origin, move 1 unit to the right, then 1 unit down. Point U lies in Quadrant IV.

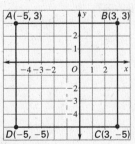

8. Points A, B, C, and D form a square. The perimeter is 32 units.

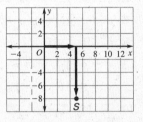

Problem Solving Workshop: Mixed Problem Solving

1. a. $\ell = 5 - (-3) = 8$, $w = 3 - (-3) = 6$
b. $P = 28$ units, $A = 48$ square units
c. $P = 280$ feet, $A = 4800$ square feet

2. a. 7.50, 10, 12.50

b–c. 8 gallons of gasoline cost about $20.

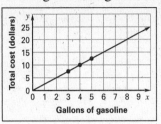

3. Answers will vary. *Sample Answer:*
$(-2, -3)$, $(2, 1)$

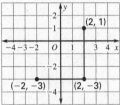

4. 57.30   **5.** The profit is the sell price minus the cost for the plain pizza and for the pepperoni times the number of pizzas sold minus the cost to rent the stand. Let x be the number of pizzas sold.

$$[8 - (4.25 + 0.75)]x - 30 = [8 - 5]x - 30$$
$$= 3x - 30$$

An expression for the profit the band will make is $3x - 30$ where x is the number of pizzas sold.

6. a. $7x + 4x + 120$; $(7 + 4)x + 120$
b. 285, 340 **c.** Answers will vary.

7. $P = 32$ units; $A(0, -4)$, $B(0, 2)$, $C(2, 2)$, $D(2, 5)$, $E(7, 5)$, and $F(7, -4)$

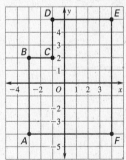

Challenge Practice

1. II **2.** IV **3.** I and III **4.** I and II **5.** II and IV

Lesson 2.8 *continued*

6.
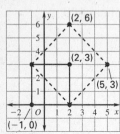

7. (2, 3), (−1, 0)

8. (5, 3), (2, 6)

9.

x	y	(x, y)
−2	−2	(−2, −2)
−1	−3	(−1, −3)
0	−4	(0, −4)
1	−3	(1, −3)
2	−2	(2, −2)
3	−1	(3, −1)

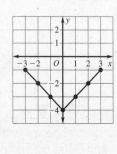

Chapter Review Games and Activities

1. (2, 4) **2.** (5, 5) **3.** (2.5, 2.5) **4.** (9, 0)

5. (4, −2) **6.** (5, −5) **7.** (2, −4) **8.** (0, −9)

9. (−2, −4) **10.** (−5, −5) **11.** (−2.5, −2.5)

12. (−9, 0) **13–21.** Check students' work.

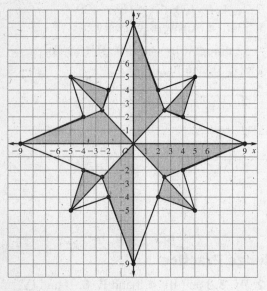

Real Life Project

1. $936 **2.** −$9 **3.** $227 **4.** Check students' report form, actual daily report, and research source(s).

Cooperative Project

1. 12 points to 42 points **2.** 96 points

3. Check students' games.

Independent Extra Credit Project

Check students' posters.

Cumulative Practice

1. 18–24 year olds **2.** 65 years old and older

3. about 50 people **4.** 12 **5.** 6 **6.** 14 **7.** 25

8. 42 **9.** 2 **10.** 21 − x **11.** 7x **12.** x + 4

13. x − 6 **14.** w = 4 **15.** s = 30 **16.** x = 3

17. y = 8 **18.** n = 12 **19.** t = 28

20. 24 cm; 27 cm^2 **21.** 68 ft; 240 ft^2

22. 24 in.; 36 in.^{2} **23.** $160 **24.** > **25.** <

26. > **27.** > **28.** = **29.** = **30.** −22

31. 9 **32.** −42 **33.** −7 **34.** 33 **35.** −42 **36.** 56

37. −48 **38.** −21 **39.** −9 **40.** 3 **41.** 0

42. 0; Identity Property of Addition

43. 4; Associative Property of Addition **44.** y; Commutative Property of Addition **45.** 1; Identity Property of Multiplication **46.** 2c + 15d

47. −10x + 6 **48.** −2x + 13y + 6

49. −u − 3 **50.** 5x + 20 **51.** 6y − 6

52. 63 + 36 = 99 **53.** 24 + (−12) = 12

54. −8t − 16 **55.** −6u − 6v + 18 **56.** (−3, 1)

57. (−1, 0) **58.** (3, 2) **59.** (4, 0) **60.** (2, −2)

61. (0, −3)

62–67.
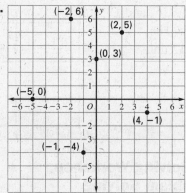

62. Quadrant II **63.** Quadrant IV **64.** y-axis

65. Quadrant III **66.** x-axis **67.** Quadrant I